PUB
TIME

TRIVIA

AMAZING INVENTORY OF INCREDIBLE KNOWLEDGE

CONTENTS

THINK YOU KNOW A THING OR TWO?

Prepare to find out. This book throws a little of everything at you—fifteen chapters of random trivia topics ranging from general history, culture, and the arts to medical esoterica and bygone college football champions. It's a deceptive mix of the tricky and the mundane. If you're a trivia buff, you'll love the challenge. And you're bound to be surprised by some of the facts we've uncovered.

You'll find questions on the right-hand pages and answers on the following pages (along with a bit of additional information). Each chapter has a theme, making it easy for you to pick whatever topic is the toughest or most interesting to you (or your opponent). If music is your thing, head to chapter two. If you think you know which president went skinny-dipping in the Potomoc, try Americana. And be prepared—we're not above a few trick questions!

So grab a chair, pull out *Pub Time Trivia,* and get ready for an entertaining night.

1. Which of the following was not one of the General Mills monster cereals?

A. Fruit Brute

B. Boo Berry

C. Zombie Puffs

D. Yummy Mummy

2. Which of the following was not a limited-edition flavor of Jones Soda?

A. Turkey & Gravy

B. Salmon Paté

C. Antacid

D. Roasted Garlic Hummus

1. **C.** And it's too bad, because Zombie Puffs would have fit right in with Count Chocula, Franken Berry, and the rest of the gang.

2. **D.** We'd rather drink that than the Seahawks Collector Pack flavors Perspiration, Natural Field Turf, and Dirt...but just barely.

3. ONIONS

BELONG TO WHAT FLOWER FAMILY?

A. Lily
B. Rose
C. Sunflower
D. Hyacinth

4. True OR false?

The adhesive on a lickable U.S. postage stamp contains ten calories.

3.

A. Also in this very pungent family: garlic, leeks, and chives.

4. **False.** That little baby is a dietary bargain at only one-tenth of a calorie.

5. If you went to a diner and ordered a **"Burn the British,"** what would you get?

A. Hard-boiled eggs
B. Toasted English muffins
C. French toast
D. Short stack of pancakes

6. Although milk is the state's official drink, sometimes Nebraskans have a taste for something a little less natural, so they indulge in the state's official state soft drink. What is it?

A. Kool-Aid
B. Pepsi
C. Country Time Lemonade
D. Dr. Pepper

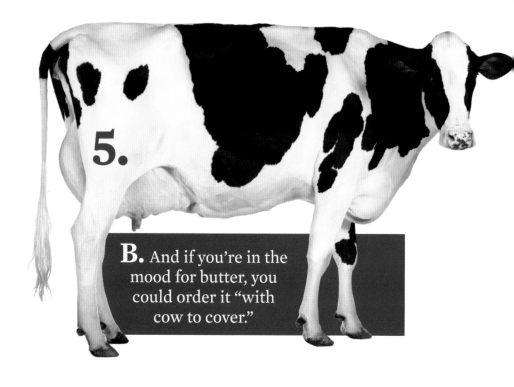

5.

B. And if you're in the mood for butter, you could order it "with cow to cover."

6. **A.** No word on whether Kool-Aid Man had to bust through the walls at the state capitol to make it happen, but Kool-Aid was designated the official soft drink in 1998.

7. *WHICH CREEPY ACTOR* also penned a gourmet cookbook?

A. John Malkovich

B. Bela Lugosi

C. Willem Dafoe

D. Vincent Price

8. **Which of these is not an actual week dedicated to an offbeat food?**

A. Solo Diners Eat Out Week

B. Eat Dessert First Week

C. Stuff Yourself Silly Week

D. Gluten-Free Baking Week

7. **D.** Long before he did the voiceover for Michael Jackson's "Thriller," Price and his wife, Mary, penned the terrifyingly good *A Treasury of Great Recipes* (1965).

8. **C.** To be fair, though, there is an Eat What You Want Day (May 11). Everything in moderation, just like we always say.

9. Which of these is not an actual flavor of a classic soda fountain drink?

A. Burn One in the Hay

B. Shake One in the Hay

C. Burn One All the Way

D. Shake One All the Way

10. Is it ever hot enough to actually FRY AN EGG on the sidewalk?

9. **A.** Burn One All the Way is a chocolate malted; Shake One in the Hay is a strawberry milkshake; and Shake One All the Way is a chocolate milkshake.

10.

NO. At its hottest, even blacktop falls about 13 degrees Fahrenheit short of the 158 degrees Fahrenheit needed to host your own outdoor fry-up.

11. Twist-ties (and plastic tabs) on bread sold in stores are color-coded. Why?

A. To tell which worker packaged the bread

B. To tell the date the bread was baked

C. To confuse consumers

D. To identify the bakery where the bread was baked

12. True OR false?

The Vaportini is a cocktail that you inhale instead of drink.

11. **B.** Much to the gratitude of stock clerks everywhere, it's much easier to pick out all the twist ties of a certain color than to squint at the tiny sell-by dates on the packages when it comes time to take old bread off the shelf.

12. TRUE. The alcoholic experience was invented at Red Kiva, a Chicago cocktail lounge. A candle is used to heat up liquid spirits, the vapors from which are then captured in a glass ball at the top of the glass and inhaled through a straw.

13. What do these food phrases all have in common?

A. Go hang a salami. I'm a lasagna hog.

B. A nut for a jar of tuna.

C. Ana, nab a banana.

D. Murder for a jar of red rum.

14. You're milking a cow. How many squirts of milk from the udders does it take to make a gallon

?

13. They're all palindromes—words or phrases that read the same forward and backward.

14. Between 340 and 350. Now imagine doing that for 10 or 15 cows twice a day for years, and you might have the makings of a farmer.

15. In 2013, Texas joined a short list of states by naming the pecan pie the official state pie. Match these other states with their official state pies.

1. Florida
2. Vermont
3. Massachusetts
4. Indiana
5. Delaware

A. Sugar cream
B. Boston cream
C. Key lime
D. Peach
E. Apple

16.

Refreshing lemon-lime soda 7-Up originally counted which substance among its ingredients?

A. Cocaine
B. Lithium
C. Valium
D. Heroin

15. 1. C; 2. E; 3. B; 4. A; 5. D.

16. B. "It's an UP thing," indeed.

17. True OR false?

No matter how big the ear, there are always an odd number of rows of kernels on each ear of corn.

18.

At a price of more than $300 per pound, kopi luwak is the world's most expensive coffee. What makes these coffee beans so special?

A. Each bean is hand-roasted over an open flame.

B. Beans are only picked on the night of a blue moon.

C. Beans are picked out of animal droppings.

D. There are only five acres of fields in the world suited to grow these beans.

17. FALSE. Because the female flowers of corn kernels occur in pairs, there is always an even number of rows of kernels. The better to sink your teeth into!

18.

C. Civet cats eat the coffee cherries but can't digest the beans, so they pass through the animal's digestive tract and then are, um, handpicked and readied for roasting.

MUSIC

1. **Which fairy tale inspired Duran Duran's hit song "Hungry Like the Wolf"?**

A. The Wolf and the Seven Little Kids

B. The Three Little Pigs

C. The Wolf and the Man

D. Little Red Riding Hood

2. **In the Simon and Garfunkel song of the same name, why does the narrator need to go "Somewhere They Can't Find Me"?**

A. He had a fight with his brother.

B. He robbed a liquor store.

C. He escaped from prison.

D. His lover broke his heart.

1. **D.** "Hungry Like the Wolf" was the second single from the 1982 album *Rio*.

2. **B.** The narrator leaves his lover in the middle of the night to avoid being arrested.

3. Metallica's 1990s smash hit **"Enter Sandman"** features the repeating lyric "We're off to never-never land." What lyric did singer James Hetfield originally write instead of this catchphrase?

A. "Maybe it's not meant to be."

B. "Disrupt the perfect family."

C. "Dream in perfect ecstasy."

D. "Nightmares help you really see."

4. U2's hit song "Pride (In the Name of Love)" features these lyrics in reference to the assassination of Dr. Martin Luther King, Jr.: "Early morning, April four/Shot rings out in the Memphis sky." Why shouldn't listeners rely on Bono for their history lessons?

A. King wasn't killed in Memphis.

B. King died in May.

C. The assassination took place in the evening.

D. King wasn't shot.

3. **B.** The band decided the lyric was too dark for the song to succeed and convinced Hetfield to change it— and the rest, as they say, is RIAA Certified Platinum single history.

4. **C.** Bono now sings, "Early evening, April four" in live shows.

5. Match the rapper with his or her stage name.

1. Shawntae Harris
2. Curtis Jackson
3. Dana Owens
4. Calvin Broadus
5. Shawn Carter

A. 50 Cent
B. Snoop Dogg
C. Jay Z
D. Da Brat
E. Queen Latifah

6. What patriotically titled album was the first compact disc ever made in the UNITED STATES?

A. *Breakfast in America*, Supertramp
B. *America (The Way I See It)*, Hank Williams, Jr.
C. *Born in the U.S.A.*, Bruce Springsteen
D. *Back in the USA*, MC5

5. 1. D; 2. A; 3. E; 4. B; 5. C.

6. C. The Boss's 1984 release shares the record for most top ten hits (seven) from a single album with *Thriller* (Michael Jackson, 1982) and *Rhythm Nation 1814* (Janet Jackson, 1989).

7. Who was the inspiration for the dude in Aerosmith's
"Dude (Looks Like a Lady)" **?**

A. Vince Neil (Mötley Crüe)

B. Jon Bon Jovi (Bon Jovi)

C. Dee Snider (Twisted Sister)

D. Sebastian Bach (Skid Row)

8. Who is the only male country music star to have exceeded ten million sales for four different albums?

A. Johnny Cash

B. Garth Brooks

C. Willie Nelson

D. Kenny Chesney

7. **A.** The song was released in 1987 at the height of the "hair bands." Go ahead, Google it. We'll wait.

8. **B.** Perhaps his "Friends in Low Places" were hanging out at the record shop.

9.

WHICH BAND DID NOT FEATURE LEGENDARY GUITARIST

ERIC CLAPTON?

A. The Yardbirds

B. Traffic

C. Cream

D. Derek and the Dominos

10.

Which of these musical acts turned down the chance to perform at the 1969 Woodstock Music and Art Festival?

A. The Grateful Dead

B. Sly & the Family Stone

C. Jethro Tull

D. Jefferson Airplane

9. **B.** Steve Winwood, who formed Traffic with three friends, later went on to form the band Blind Faith with Clapton.

10. **B.** In an interview, front man Ian Anderson cited his aversion to hippies and spontaneous outdoor nudity as reasons for turning down the gig.

11. Which of these musicians is not a native Canadian?

A. Alanis Morissette

B. Neil Young

C. Celine Dion

D. Van Morrison

12. What American city is most associated with grunge music?

A. New York

B. Memphis

C. Seattle

D. Minneapolis

11. **D.** The "Brown Eyed Girl" singer was born in Belfast, Ireland.

12. **C.** Seattle produced grunge rockers Pearl Jam, Alice in Chains, Soundgarden, and of course, Nirvana.

13. Ozzy Osbourne was famously banned from the city of San Antonio for a decade. What did he do to earn his banishment?

A. Bit the head off a live bat in a concert there

B. Gave a lewd, nude public performance

C. Urinated on the Alamo

D. Started a riot

14. Which piano-playing entertainer earned the nicknames "Mr. Showmanship" & "The Glitter Man"?

A. Stevie Wonder

B. Liberace

C. Elton John

D. Billy Joel

13. **C.** Osbourne acted in a drunken stupor, but later made up with the city by donating $20,000 to the Daughters of the Republic of Texas to help restore the national landmark. We bet Ozzy doesn't have any trouble remembering the Alamo these days!

14. **B.** Liberace's legendary bedazzled pianos were no match for his wardrobe, which included such gems as a blue fox cape that trailed 16 feet behind him and a King Neptune costume that weighed 200 pounds.

15. Which musical genre has the most radio stations in the United States

A. Rock
B. Top 40
C. Country
D. Oldies

16. Music legend **BOB DYLAN** had what body part insured by Lloyd's of London?

A. Vocal cords
B. Throat
C. Hands
D. Fingers

15. **C.** There are nearly 2,000 country stations around the country. That's a lot of twang!

16. **A.** Dylan was apparently worried that the day would come when he would stop blowin' in the wind.

17. Which height-challenged singer was parodied in an infamous basketball skit on **Chappelle's Show?**

A. David Bowie

B. Cee Lo Green

C. Lil Wayne

D. Prince

18. *Which former Beatle was the first person to be featured on the cover of* **Rolling Stone?**

A. George Harrison

B. Paul McCartney

C. John Lennon

D. Ringo Starr

17. **D.** In the skit, Charlie Murphy tells a story about being beaten in basketball by Prince and his crew, who were still wearing their stage costumes (picture a purple velvet suit and heeled boots). After the skit aired, Prince said in interviews that while he wasn't really wearing a costume, he really did school Murphy on the court.

18. **C.** No, it wasn't the naked picture with Yoko Ono—in 1967, Lennon was featured in a still from the film *How I Won the War*.

GOVERNMENT

1. Which of the following movies did President Ronald Reagan NOT star in?

A. *The Voice of the Turtle*

B. *Hellcats of the Navy*

C. *Girls on Probation*

D. *Million Dollar Baby*

2. Which British ruler's skeleton was discovered under a parking lot in 2012?

A. Henry VIII

B. Richard III

C. Lord Fauntleroy

D. King Ralph

1. Trick question: Ronnie was in all of them! *Million Dollar Baby* is also the title of a 1941 film about a department store worker who is given—you guessed it—a million dollars. It's more like *Shopgirl* meets *It Could Happen to You* than the 2004 Clint Eastwood-directed boxing film. Don't be so surprised. Reagan once starred opposite a chimpanzee in *Bedtime for Bonzo*.

2. **B.** Now that Richard III's remains have been found, historians seek to further challenge previously held ideas brought about by William Shakespeare's play and his Tudor successors. It was once thought that Richard III was hunchbacked; now it appears he merely had a curved spine.

3. True OR false?

The American flag must be burned if it touches the ground.

4. In 2013, Senator Rand Paul made news when he filibustered Congress by talking for 12 hours and 52 minutes, marking the ninth-longest filibuster on record. Who holds the record for the longest filibuster of the U.S. Congress?

A. Barney Frank

B. Ron Paul

C. Ruth Baker Pratt

D. Strom Thurmond

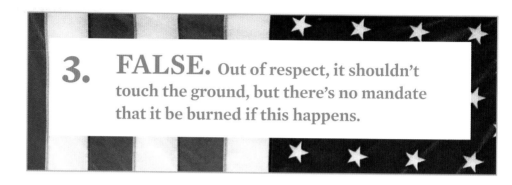

3. **FALSE.** Out of respect, it shouldn't touch the ground, but there's no mandate that it be burned if this happens.

4. **D.** The late South Carolina senator Strom Thurmond spoke against the 1957 Civil Rights Act for 24 hours and 18 minutes. What a waste of time. At least Rand Paul was questioning our government's use of drones on American soil.

5. *HOW MANY AMENDMENTS ARE THERE TO THE U.S. CONSTITUTION?*

A. 19

B. 23

C. 27

D. 31

6. What color is the bottom stripe on the American flag? You don't need the colors listed, do you?

5. **C.** The last amendment added to the Constitution enacted new rules about when salary changes for members of Congress can take effect. The amendment was submitted to the states for ratification in 1789 and adopted in 1992. How's that for progress?

6. **RED.** *There are thirteen alternating stripes, seven red and six white. But do you know how many stars are in the bottom row? (Six. Five rows of six stars alternate with four rows of five stars, for a grand total of 50 stars.)*

7. Which of the following is headquartered in
LANGLEY, VIRGINIA?

A. Central Intelligence Agency **(CIA)**

B. Department of Homeland Security **(DHS)**

C. Federal Bureau of Investigation **(FBI)**

D. Internal Revenue Service **(IRS)**

8. Who ran against George W. Bush for the presidency in **2004**?

A. Hillary Clinton

B. John Kerry

C. Al Gore

D. Joe Biden

7. **A.** The headquarters of the other three agencies are all in Washington, D.C. Spies do tend to be loners.

8. **B.** Between the 2000 election and 2004 election, only three states changed their party alignment. New Mexico and Iowa voted for Al Gore in 2000 and then for Bush in 2004, and New Hampshire voted for Bush in 2000 and then for Kerry in 2004. Bush's voting numbers were the highest until President Barack Obama's totals in 2008 and 2012, but he still retains the highest amount for any Republican presidential nominee.

9. What was the title bestowed on Kate Middleton when she married Prince William?

A. Duchess of Cambridge

B. Duchess of Cornwall

C. Duchess of York

D. Princess Catherine

10. Who was the first U.S. president to be **impeached**?

A. Andrew Johnson

B. James K. Polk

C. Richard Nixon

D. Bill Clinton

9. **A.** *Judging by tabloid shorthand, you might've thought she followed in Madonna, Cher, and Adele's footsteps to become simply Kate.*

10. **A.** Johnson was Abraham Lincoln's vice president and succeeded Lincoln following his assassination. Johnson was impeached by the House of Representatives, though the act failed in the U.S. Senate. Johnson was impeached for violating the Tenure of Office Act that had been enacted the year before, which he vetoed and Congress passed anyway.

11. WHO WAS THE *DIRECTOR OF THE FBI* FOR ALMOST HALF OF THE 20TH CENTURY?

A. Winston Churchill

B. Allen Dulles

C. J. Edgar Hoover

D. Howard Hughes

12. Which celebrity was Al Gore's college roommate at Harvard?

A. Billy Crystal

B. Tommy Lee Jones

C. Steven Spielberg

D. Henry Winkler

11. **C.** Hoover was appointed in 1924 and held the position until his death in 1972. He began the world's largest fingerprint file, a scientific detection lab, and the FBI National Academy, among many other accomplishments. He also used the organization's secret files to benefit himself by blackmailing politicians to secure his powerful position.

12. **B.** *Can you imagine the former vice president and Agent K from* Men in Black *hanging out between classes?*

13. True OR false?

The only people who appear on common U.S. currency are presidents.

14. What is the official title for the political leader of AUSTRALIA?

A. President

B. Prime Minister

C. Chancellor

D. Supreme Commander

13. **FALSE.** Alexander Hamilton appears on the $10 bill, and Benjamin Franklin is on the $100 bill. We all know that Franklin was a real Renaissance man (an author, scientist, postmaster, and inventor, among other things), but what did Hamilton do? Only served as the first Secretary of the Treasury and opened the U.S. Mint.

14. **B.** But Australia is a part of the Commonwealth realms, which makes Queen Elizabeth II of England the nation's reigning monarch. Her full title there is Elizabeth the Second, by the Grace of God, Queen of Australia and Her other Realms and Territories, Head of the Commonwealth. Conversely, the position of Prime Minister is not mentioned in the Constitution of Australia and is merely an unwritten custom.

15.

WHAT DOES
THE "**S**" IN
HARRY S. TRUMAN
STAND FOR?

A. Shipp

B. Stuyvesant

C. Solomon

D. It doesn't stand for anything

16. *Who was the only United States president to remain a bachelor while in office?*

A. James Buchanan

B. John Tyler

C. Benjamin Harrison

D. Millard Fillmore

15. **D.** The "S" did not stand for a name, though it alluded to both of Truman's grandfather's names—Anderson Shipp Truman and Solomon Young.

16. **A.** While Buchanan was the fifteenth president of the United States, he was engaged to Ann Caroline Coleman. Buchanan was extremely busy with his political work during their engagement, so Ann broke it off. She died shortly thereafter. Buchanan's niece Harriet Lane was the lady of the house during his term as president.

17. *How many stars of the 1987 sci-fi film* Predator *went on to become state governors?*

18. For how long did vice presidential nominee Sarah Palin serve as **GOVERNOR OF ALASKA?**

A. 965 days

B. 156 weeks

C. 48 months

D. 6 years

17. **Two.** Arnold Schwarzenegger went on to become the Governator of California; professional-wrestler Jesse "The Body" Ventura went on to become governor of Minnesota. *Saturday Night Live* writer and star Al Franken became a senator for Minnesota as well. Minnesotans must like their politicians good and famous.

18. **A.** Palin was governor from December 4, 2006, until she resigned on July 26, 2009. For comparison, the first time Tina Fey parodied the politician on *Saturday Night Live* was September 13, 2008, and the last time was May 8, 2011— a span of 967 days!

FOOTBALL

1. Fans of which NFL team might be found in the "Dawg Pound" at home games?

A. Cincinnati Bengals

B. Pittsburgh Steelers

C. Cleveland Browns

D. Houston Texans

2. Though he played only nine seasons, which Hall of Fame running back was named NFL MVP three times and averaged an amazing 5.2 yards per carry during his career?

1. **C.** Rabid fans in the bleacher seats at Cleveland Browns games refer to their area as the

"DAWG POUND."

2. **Jim Brown. The Cleveland Browns great led the NFL in rushing in all but one of his nine campaigns.**

3. True OR false?

The Buffalo Bills were the first team to lose four Super Bowl games.

4. Which of the following NFL franchises originated in the city in which it still plays?

A. Dallas Cowboys

B. Arizona Cardinals

C. Indianapolis Colts

D. St. Louis Rams

3. **FALSE.** Before the New England Patriots, Buffalo Bills, or Denver Broncos lost their fourth ones, the Minnesota Vikings "accomplished" the dubious feat by losing four of the first 11 Super Bowls played.

4. **A.** The Cowboys were founded in Dallas in 1960. The Cardinals were born in Chicago and moved to St. Louis; the Colts started in Baltimore; and the Rams wound up in St. Louis via Cleveland and Los Angeles.

5. *Which of these college football greats did not win the* **Heisman Trophy?**

A. Bo Jackson
B. Herschel Walker
C. Joe Theismann
D. Billy Sims

6. **WHICH SCHOOL HAS WON THE MOST NATIONAL CHAMPIONSHIPS IN FOOTBALL?**

A. Alabama
B. Notre Dame
C. Oklahoma
D. Princeton

5. **C.** Though he changed the pronunciation of his name to rhyme with the fabled award while quarterbacking Notre Dame, Theismann was runner-up to Jim Plunkett in the 1970 Heisman voting.

6. **D.** You might be surprised to hear it, but Princeton claims 28 national titles—beginning in 1869—although debate exists about the "mythical" nature of those championships.

7. **Name the *legendary* coach who won more than 88 percent of his games.**

8. Who was the first player to win the Heisman Trophy twice?

A. Bo Jackson

B. Archie Griffin

C. Charles White

D. Tim Brown

7. **Knute Rockne.** The Notre Dame coach, with a 105–12–5 career mark, holds the record for winning percentage in both the college and pro ranks.

8. **B.** *Griffin, the Ohio State running back, won the award in 1974 and '75.*

9. Who was the first freshman to win the Heisman Trophy

A. Johnny Manziel

B. Charles Woodson

C. Vinny Testaverde

D. Glenn Davis

10. Emmitt Smith became the NFL's career rushing leader during his brilliant career between 1990 and 2004. Who previously held the record?

A. Jim Brown

B. Barry Sanders

C. Walter Payton

D. Tony Dorsett

9. **A.** In 2013, Texas A&M quarterback **"Johnny Football"** became the first frosh to win the award.

10. **C.** Payton was the only man in NFL history to rush for more than 16,000 career yards before Smith came along and topped 18,000.

11. True OR false?

Knute Rockne is considered the
"father of American football."

12. WHAT NICKNAME DO THE STADIUMS OF CLEMSON AND LSU SHARE?

11. **FALSE.** Walter Camp, who coached at Stanford and Yale, holds that distinction for his role in shaping the game as we know it.

12. Death Valley. And debate has gone on for years among fans about which home field is the "true" Death Valley.

13. *Which of the following college football awards is given annually to a defensive player?*

A. Maxwell Award
B. Davey O'Brien Award
C. Chuck Bednarik Award
D. Lou Groza Award

14. **Which of the following *SUPER BOWL-WINNING* quarterbacks was chosen Lowest in the NFL Draft?**

A. Joe Montana
B. Joe Flacco
C. Brad Johnson
D. Tom Brady

13. **C.** The **Chuck Bednarik Award** is given to the Defensive Player of the Year.

14. **C.** Flacco was a first-rounder, Montana a third-rounder and Brady a sixth-rounder. Brad Johnson, though, was a ninth-round choice out of Florida State in 1992 who went on to quarterback the 2002 Tampa Bay Buccaneers to a Super Bowl victory.

15. In the era of the AP poll (since 1936), who was the first coach to win Division I national championships at two different schools?

A. Urban Meyer
B. Jim Tressel
C. Lou Holtz
D. Nick Saban

16. *What does* **BCS** *stand for?*

15.

D. Saban won titles at LSU and Alabama to earn this distinction.

16.

Bowl Championship Series

17. Which college football rivalry has been played the most times?

A. Army-Navy
B. Lafayette-Lehigh
C. Notre Dame-Southern Cal
D. Ohio State-Michigan

18. True OR false?

The winner of the annual Army-Navy game is awarded the Commander-in-Chief's Trophy.

17. **B.** These Eastern Pennsylvania neighbors have been doing gridiron battle since 1884.

18.

FALSE. In addition to Army and Navy, Air Force is also eligible in this round-robin competition among service academies.

19. Name the kicker who led all NFL scorers in 1998 while making every single field goal and extra-point attempt, helping his team lead the league in total points.

A. Morten Andersen

B. Gary Anderson

C. Steve Christie

D. Al Del Greco

20. *Which player, during the 1980s, '90s and 2000s, set virtually every Super Bowl receiving record?*

19. **B.** Anderson enjoyed a perfect season for the Minnesota Vikings by going 35-for-35 on field goals and 59-for-59 on extra points, totaling 164 points.

20. *Jerry Rice of the San Francisco 49ers, and later the Oakland Raiders, set records for catches, yards, and receiving touchdowns in a game and career.*

21. What annual game is known as the
Iron Bowl?

A. Yale-Princeton

B. Michigan-Notre Dame

C. Auburn-Alabama

D. Army-Navy

22. *After suffering a serious knee injury in 2011, which running back made an amazing comeback to lead the NFL with a near-record 2,097 rushing yards and 2,314 yards from scrimmage in 2012?*

A. Adrian Peterson

B. Jamaal Charles

C. Marshawn Lynch

D. Doug Martin

21. C. The Auburn-Alabama series dates to 1892, and was named the Iron Bowl in honor of Birmingham, which sits on vast deposits of iron ore.

22. A. Peterson came within nine yards of Eric Dickerson's single-season rushing record in his stunning return to the Minnesota Vikings.

23. Which of the following college football stars went on to play professional basketball?

A. Charlie Ward
B. Deion Sanders
C. Joe Montana
D. Bo Jackson

24. Which school, by a margin of almost 100 games, holds the NCAA record for most consecutive sold-out home games?

23.

A. While Sanders and Jackson played pro baseball, it was Florida State's Ward who starred on the hardwood for the New York Knicks.

24. Nebraska.
The Cornhuskers sold out against Missouri in 1962 and have not had an unsold seat since.

25. Despite leading the NFL in number of times being sacked, which player posted the highest QB rating during the 2012 regular season?

A. Eli Manning
B. Russell Wilson
C. Aaron Rodgers
D. Peyton Manning

26. # True OR false?

Brett Favre owns the record for longest touchdown pass in Super Bowl history, an 81-yard strike to Antonio Freeman.

25. **C.** Rodgers was sacked a league-leading 51 times in 2012, but still posted a QB rating of 108 while leading his injury-depleted Packers to an NFC North crown.

26. **FALSE.** Favre did set the record with that pass to Freeman in 1997, but seven years later Carolina Panthers QB Jake Delhomme broke it with an 85-yard scoring pass to Muhsin Muhammad.

27. After being drafted in the 10th round in 1964 and serving a tour in the U.S. Navy, which quarterback joined the Dallas Cowboys and ultimately turned them into Super Bowl champions?

A. Tony Romo
B. Danny White
C. Drew Bledsoe
D. Roger Staubach

28. *WHO, IN 2012, BROKE JOHNNY UNITAS' LONGSTANDING RECORD FOR CONSECUTIVE GAMES THROWING AT LEAST ONE TOUCHDOWN PASS?*

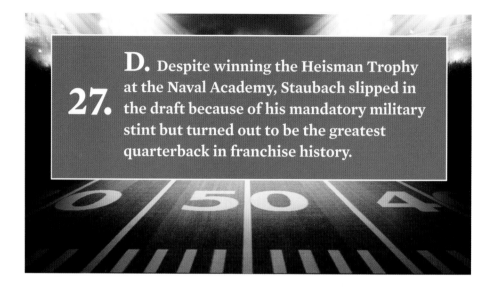

27. **D.** Despite winning the Heisman Trophy at the Naval Academy, Staubach slipped in the draft because of his mandatory military stint but turned out to be the greatest quarterback in franchise history.

28. DREW BREES.

The New Orleans Saints QB threw at least one scoring pass in 54 consecutive games before a November loss to the Atlanta Falcons.

29. Which college football rivalry, thanks to its tailgate parties, is affectionately known as the *"World's Largest Outdoor Cocktail Party"*?

A. LSU-Alabama
B. Ohio State-Michigan
C. Texas-Texas A&M
D. Florida-Georgia

30. Only 11 players are allowed on the field at a time, but which school goes all-out to celebrate its *"12th Man"* tradition?

A. Texas
B. Texas A&M
C. Notre Dame
D. Oregon

29. D. The SEC rivalry between the Gators and Bulldogs inspires this refreshing moniker.

30. B. *Texas A&M allows a distinguished "unsung" player to wear jersey no. 12 in honor of the tradition.*

31. When he started his 117th consecutive game in 1999, which player did Brett Favre overtake to become the new NFL "Iron Man"

A. Dan Marino

B. Terry Bradshaw

C. Joe Ferguson

D. Ron Jaworski

32. True OR false?

The Chicago Bears have won more NFL games than any team in history.

31. **D.** Ron Jaworski set the previous mark of 116 games before breaking his leg in 1984. By the time Favre officially retired in 2011, he had stretched the record to 297 games in a row.

32. **TRUE.** The Chicago Bears have been racking up wins since 1920, and after the 2014 season had 11 more wins than their nearest rival, the Green Bay Packers.

THE HUMAN BODY

1. In which field of medicine is amniocentesis used?

A. Obstetrics
B. Cardiology
C. Orthopedics
D. Urology

2. Which famous actor is a great example of heterochromia?

A. Tom Cruise
B. Julia Roberts
C. Tom Hanks
D. Jane Seymour

1. **A.** This test screens for potential problems with a fetus—and can tell gender.

2. **D.** Seymour has eyes that are two different colors: one is brown and the other is green.

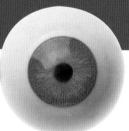

3. *How many different shades of the color **gray** can the human eye distinguish?*

4. **What was the first human organ to be successfully transplanted?**

A. Lung

B. Kidney

C. Heart

D. Liver

3. *50 SHADES OF GREY? BAH. EYES CAN DETECT ABOUT 500 DIFFERENT SHADES OF THE COLOR.*

4. **B.** The first successful transplant took place in 1954 in Boston. Since the surgery predated the discovery of anti-rejection drugs, it was a good thing the patients were identical twins so the organ was not rejected.

5. **What does the *"little brother cure"* for hiccups involve?**

A. Crossing your eyes
B. Pulling the sides of your mouth outward with both index fingers
C. Mimicking each word said by someone older than you
D. Sticking out your tongue

6. **In what part of the body can you find the only bone that is not connected to any other bones?**

A. Wrist
B. Lungs
C. Throat
D. Pelvis

5. **D.** This stimulates the glottis, the opening of the airway to the lungs. Since a closed glottis is the usual cause of hiccups, this treatment generally works.

6. **C.** The hyoid bone, which helps support the tongue when talking, is connected only by ligaments.

7. WHAT PART OF YOUR BODY WOULD YOU USE FOR GURNING ?

A. Hands

B. Abs

C. Face

D. Shoulders

8.

What is the largest muscle in the body?

A. Pectoralis major

B. Gluteus maximus

C. Adductor longus

D. Gastrocnemius

7. **C.** Gurning is a contest in which professionals compete to see who can pull the "world's ugliest face." Those who practice enough might make it to the Egremont Gurning Championship, held every September in Cumbria, England.

8. **B.** All that junk is there to support your trunk.

9. Will coffee sober you up?

10. Which of these techniques could not be used to identify a specific person?

A. Eye scan

B. Tongue print

C. Nose print

D. Fingerprint

9. No amount of coffee, soda, water, or anything other than time will do the trick. So if you've been drinking, spend your money on a cab rather than a cappuccino.

10. **C.** Nose printing can be used to identify pets and livestock, but humans mostly just leave indistinct smudges.

11. Which item is responsible for most cases of choking in the United States?

A. Pen/pencil
B. Toothpick
C. Peanut
D. Carrot

12. WHAT IS THE MOST COMMON *PLASTIC SURGERY* IN AMERICA?

A. Nose job
B. Breast augmentation
C. Liposuction
D. Face-lift

11. **B.** Maybe stick to floss next time...

12. **C.** Be prepared: Getting the fat sucked out of your abdomen, buttocks, hips, thighs, or upper arms will suck about $2,300 out of your wallet.

13. How long does it take for food to travel from the mouth to the stomach?

A. 7 seconds

B. 32 seconds

C. 1 minute

D. 3 minutes

14. True **OR** false?

Fingernails and toenails grow at the same speed.

13. **B.** And it doesn't take much longer from the lips to the hips!

14. **FALSE.** Fingernails grow two to three times faster than toenails.

15. WHAT DO THE CONES IN THE EYES HELP YOU DO?

A. See at greater distances
B. See in color
C. See nearby objects
D. See in black and white

16. Which lung is larger than the other?

15. **B.** Each eye has 6 to 7 million cones to help you find just the right shade of blue.

16. The right—the left has to accommodate the heart.

17. Can a hair test show if you smoked marijuana?

18. True **OR** false?

Each of your nostrils registers smell differently.

17. Hair can be tested for the presence of marijuana, but the test can't tell if you personally smoked the weed or if your hair just absorbed the chemicals from that last Phish show you went to. A urine or blood test is needed to verify that.

18. TRUE. The right nostril detects the more pleasant smells, but the left one...is more accurate.

19. *A LAUGH EXPELS AIR OUT OF THE BODY AT SPEEDS UP TO 70 MILES PER HOUR. WHAT IS THE SPEED OF THE AIR RELEASED WITH A SNEEZE?*

A. 80 miles per hour

B. 100 miles per hour

C. 120 miles per hour

D. 140 miles per hour

20. If you accidentally knock out a tooth, in what liquid should you store it to improve the chances of the dentist being able to re-implant it?

A. Beer (preferably stout)

B. Water

C. Juice

D. Milk

19. **B.** The sneeze is a powerful weapon—it can send 100,000 germs into the air in a single speedy bound!

20. **D.** *The proteins and antibacterial properties of milk keep the cells alive—definitely doing the body good.*

1. Clint Eastwood was far from the studio's first choice to "make their day" as Dirty Harry. Which of these actors was not offered the role before Eastwood?

    A. Frank Sinatra

    B. John Wayne

    C. Robert Redford

    D. Paul Newman

2. Which of these historical figures has been featured in the most movies?

    A. Jesus Christ

    B. Abraham Lincoln

    C. King Henry VIII

    D. Napoleon Bonaparte

1. **C.** When Eastwood was finally offered the role, he felt very lucky indeed.

2. **D.** The *"little general"* has more than 194 movies to his credit.

3. **Match the actors with their original names.**

1. Yul Brynner
2. Divine
3. Whoopi Goldberg
4. Kirk Douglas
5. Jane Seymour

A. Issur Demsky
B. Taidje Khan
C. Joyce Frankenberg
D. Caryn Johnson
E. Glenn Milstead

Which of these stars is not a twin?

4.

A. Scarlett Johansson (*Hitchcock*)
B. Vin Diesel (*Fast & Furious*)
C. Jon Heder (*Napoleon Dynamite*)
D. Ryan Gosling (*Gangster Squad*)

3. 1. B; 2. E; 3. D; 4. A; 5. C

^{4.} **D.**

Hey girl
(or guy!),

*Ryan Gosling's
no twin.*

5. *Six actors have played James Bond in the EON Productions official movie series. How many of them can you name?*

6. **HOW MANY ACTORS DID IT TAKE TO PORTRAY DARTH VADER IN** *STAR WARS*?

5. They are: Sean Connery, George Lazenby, Roger Moore, Timothy Dalton, Pierce Brosnan, and Daniel Craig.

6. **FOUR.** James Earl Jones provided Vader's deep, booming voice; David Prowse played the villain's body; Sebastian Shaw played the unmasked face; and sound designer Ben Burtt provided the dark lord's infamous breathing effect.

7.

Oscar winner Hilary Swank made her film debut in the campy 1992 film version of *Buffy the Vampire Slayer*. Which other future Oscar winner was part of the movie's cast?

A. Heath Ledger

B. Jamie Foxx

C. Ben Affleck

D. Adrien Brody

8.

Which classic video game character did not make a cameo appearance in Disney's **Wreck-It Ralph?**

A. Q*bert

B. Sonic the Hedgehog

C. Mario

D. Pac-Man

7.

C. Affleck had an uncredited role and only one line as "Basketball Player #10"—and five years later co-wrote the screenplay for *Good Will Hunting*, for which he earned his first Oscar. You've come a long way, Ben!!

8. **C.** His nemesis Bowser makes an appearance at a meeting of BAD-ANON (a support group for video game villains), but everyone's favorite plumber will just have to wait for the sequel to make his appearance.

9. In which of these movies is the F-bomb dropped the most?

A. *Casino*
B. *Scarface*
C. *Alpha Dog*
D. *Summer of Sam*

10. WHICH SCARY MOVIE WAS NOT BASED ON A BOOK PENNED BY *STEPHEN KING?*

A. *Carrie*
B. *Poltergeist*
C. *Children of the Corn*
D. *The Green Mile*

9.

D. When it was released in 1983, *Scarface* had a record 226 instances of the word, but Spike Lee's 1999 movie *Summer of Sam* used the F-word a whopping 435 times, or 3.06 times per minute.

10.

B. This ghost story was coauthored by another writing heavyweight named Steven—Spielberg, that is.

11. To what song does Phil Connors wake every morning in *Groundhog Day?*

A. "I Got You Babe" by Sonny and Cher

B. "Homeward Bound" by Simon and Garfunkel

C. "These Boots Are Made for Walkin'" by Nancy Sinatra

D. "California Dreamin'" by The Mamas & The Papas

12. True OR false?

In the original script for E.T. the Extra-Terrestrial, *the adorable alien dies.*

11.

A. By some estimates, Bill Murray's character wakes up to the song for a full 34 years during the film. How's that for an earworm?

12. **TRUE.** *Children hated the original ending, so director Steven Spielberg changed the script so the lovable E.T. could go back home.*

13. Arnold Schwarzenegger is one of only two California governors to have been awarded a star on the Hollywood Walk of Fame.

Who is the other?

14. *Which actor has won the most Academy Awards in the category Actor in a Leading Role?*

A. Tom Hanks

B. Jack Nicholson

C. Daniel Day-Lewis

D. Gene Hackman

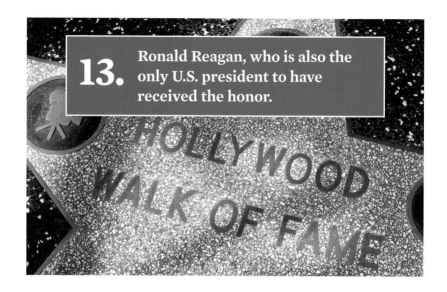

13. Ronald Reagan, who is also the only U.S. president to have received the honor.

14. **C.** Day-Lewis has three; the others have two wins in the category. Not bad for a man who has had only five film roles in the past 10 years!

15. *In how many movies did John Wayne die ?*

16. **Which of these films is not part of the *Lord of the Rings* trilogy?**

A. *The Hobbit*

B. *The Return of the King*

C. *The Fellowship of the Ring*

D. *The Two Towers*

15.

SEVEN: *Reap the Wild Wind, The Fighting Seabees, Wake of the Red Witch, Sands of Iwo Jima, The Alamo, The Cowboys,* and *The Shootist*

16. **A.** *The Hobbit: An Unexpected Journey* (2012) is part of another Peter Jackson-directed Tolkien trilogy.

17. WHAT IS THE REAL FIRST NAME OF *Indiana Jones?*

A. Max

B. Henry

C. Frank

D. Joe

18. Hedwig, Harry Potter's pet in the books and movie series, is what kind of animal?

A. Owl

B. Ferret

C. Cat

D. Guinea pig

17. **B.** The nickname came from Jones's childhood dog (who was in turn named for a dog owned by series creator George Lucas).

18. **A.** Hedwig was given to Harry as a birthday gift, and becomes his companion and messenger.

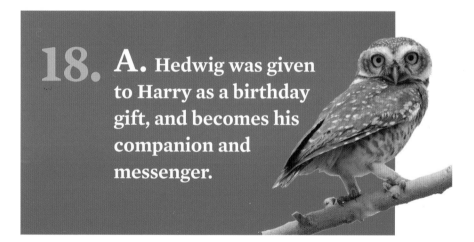

19. In the classic Mel Brooks film *Blazing Saddles* (1974), what last name is shared by all the citizens of Rock Ridge?

A. Smith

B. Jones

C. Johnson

D. Doe

20. Match the actor to the movie in which he played Santa.

1. Tim Allen

2. Billy Bob Thornton

3. Edmund Gwenn

4. Ed Asner

5. Paul Giamatti

A. *Elf*

B. *Bad Santa*

C. *Fred Claus*

D. *The Santa Clause*

E. *Miracle on 34th Street*

19. **C.** The last name emphasizes the homogeneity of the all-white town before black sheriff Bart is brought in by scheming politicos intent on destroying the town.

20.
1. D
2. B
3. E
4. A
5. C

1. What type of animal is a Holstein?

A. Cow
B. Horse
C. Pig
D. Sheep

2. True OR false?

The sting from a killer bee can be fatal.

1. **A.** Got milk? Black-and-white (or sometimes red-and-white) Holsteins are the most popular dairy cows in the United States, making up 90 percent of the total herd.

2. **TRUE.** Africanized honeybees, as killer bees are officially known, are extremely aggressive. They often attack in swarms, and their stings can kill. They are notorious for being easy to provoke and hard to escape. They will chase humans for great distances, and they've been known to stay angry for up to 24 hours.

3. *Which species contains the most poisonous animal in the world?*

A. Butterfly
B. Frog
C. Snake
D. Spider

4. Most people know that a group of lions is called a pride and a group of fish is called a school, but can you match these animals with their collective group names?

1. Apes
2. Crows
3. Jellyfish
4. Owls
5. Ravens
6. Whales

A. Murder
B. Parliament
C. Pod
D. Shrewdness
E. Smack
F. Unkindness

3. **B.** Poison dart frogs are the most poisonous animals in the world. The golden poison frog is so toxic that it's dangerous to even touch it. Just one golden poison frog has enough toxin to kill ten people. So if you find yourself in Central or South America, you might want to think twice before kissing that frog.

4. 1. D; 2. A; 3. E; 4. B; 5. F; 6. C.

5. WHAT IS STORED INSIDE A CAMEL'S HUMP ?

6. Which of the following animals was never a resident of the White House?

A. Alligator

B. Bobcat

C. Ostrich

D. Pygmy hippopotamus

5. Fat. If you thought the answer was water, you're not alone. (You're wrong, but you're not alone.) The fat stored in a camel's hump allows the animal to go for up to a month without food—pretty useful for those long treks across the desert.

6. **C.** The White House has been home to all sorts of animals—domesticated and otherwise. John Quincy Adams owned a gator that lived in the East Room for two months. Calvin Coolidge literally had a zoo at the White House, including a bobcat, a pygmy hippo, a bear, lion cubs, raccoons, a hyena, and more. Theodore Roosevelt had an extensive menagerie too.

7. Macaroni, gentoo, chinstrap, and rockhopper are types of what?

A. Butterflies
B. Dogs
C. Penguins
D. Zebras

8. Which of the following is not a type of **cat?**

A. Calico
B. Rex
C. Saluki
D. Scottish Fold

7. **C.** There are 17 breeds of penguins in the world; these are just four of them.

8. **C.** Salukis are dogs—in fact, theirs may be the oldest known breed of domesticated dog. Salukis were held in such great esteem in ancient Egypt that they were sometimes mummified along with the pharaohs.

9. Of the 12 signs of the zodiac, how many are modeled on animals?

10. *What do snakes primarily use their tongues for?*

A. Hearing

B. Seeing

C. Smelling

D. Tasting

9. **SEVEN.** Aries (ram), Taurus (bull), Cancer (crab), Leo (lion), Scorpio (scorpion), Capricorn (sea goat), and Pisces (fish) are animal signs.

10. **C.**
While snakes can use their tongues for tasting and even touching, they use them mostly for smelling.

11. ON AVERAGE, WHICH OF THE FOLLOWING SHARK SPECIES KILLS THE MOST HUMANS EACH YEAR?

A. Copper shark

B. Bull shark

C. Tiger shark

D. Mako shark

12. The pangolin, a toothless mammal found in southern Africa and Asia, is the only mammal to have which of the following reptilian characteristics?

A. Can grow back its tail

B. Has scales

C. Is cold blooded

D. Secretes venom

11. **B.** The United States averages fewer than one shark fatality every two years, while an average of 39 people are killed each year by lightning strikes. Statistically, you should be more afraid of the turf than the surf.

12. **B.** The pangolin, sometimes referred to as the scaly anteater, is the only mammal with scales. It has no teeth, and uses its powerful claws to tear open termite and ant mounds.

13. Excluding insects, which animal has the fastest metabolism?

A. Cheetah
B. Pygmy shrew
C. Hummingbird
D. Chipmunk

14. True OR false?

A jellyfish has no brain.

13. **C.** Hummingbirds, which consume more than their own body weight in nectar daily, are always mere hours away from starvation. With an average heart rate of 1,260 beats per minute, a hummingbird can slow its heart down to 50 to 180 beats per minute, allowing it to survive when food is scarce. Second place in the high metabolism race goes to the eternally hungry Eurasian pygmy shrew, which can go only ten minutes without eating.

14. **TRUE.** The jellyfish has no brain, blood, or nervous system. Jellyfish do have eyespots that can detect light and dark, as well as chemosensory pits that can identify potential predators. And don't let their name fool you—jellyfish are 95% water.

15. Which one of these frog species is able to continuously freeze and thaw throughout the winter, in order to hibernate under surface leaves?

A. Wood frog

B. Waxy monkey frog

C. Purple frog

D. Western spotted frog

16. Most people believe that Santa's reindeer are a subspecies of the bull reindeer. Both bull reindeer sexes can grow antlers—but on Christmas Eve, which sex would Santa's reindeer most likely be?

15.

A. Wood frogs are able to tolerate the extreme cold in their blood and other tissues, which allows them to freeze and thaw many times each winter as needed. Frogs also have the ability to breathe through their skin underwater, allowing oxygen to diffuse directly into their blood stream. No word on whether a kiss from an ice princess would make a frozen wood frog human or not, but don't hold your breath.

16. FEMALE.

According to the Alaska Department of Fish and Gaming, male bull reindeer shed their antlers in October, while female bull reindeer don't shed their antlers until April.

17. Which of these species is responsible for the most human fatalities on the **continent of Africa?**

A. Lion

B. Crocodile

C. Elephant

D. Hippopotamus

18. Which marsupial can give birth to more live babies than any other species?

A. Kangaroo

B. Tasmanian devil

C. Koala

D. Possum

17.

D. The male hippopotamus actively protects its territory, and females are known for aggressive behavior when their young are present. And hippos can run at speeds of up to 20 miles per hour. Next trip to Africa, pack your running shoes!

18.

B. After a 21-day gestation cycle, the Tasmanian devil can give birth to as many as 30 live young at one time. But because a mama Tasmanian devil has only four teats, her babies compete fiercely for milk. Eventually, Mom ends up eating many of her kids...whole. Aren't you glad you only got sent to your room?

19. Which of the objects listed is closest in size to the giant squid's eye, the largest eye in the animal kingdom?

A. Baseball

B. Basketball

C. Bass drum

D. Monster-truck tire

20. VERY FEW MAMMALS ARE POISONOUS, BUT ONE OF THESE IS. WHICH ONE?

A. Beaver

B. Sloth

C. Kangaroo

D. Platypus

19. **B.** The giant squid's eye needs to be this large so it can detect one of its main predators, the sperm whale. The largest giant squid on record was 43 feet long. Not until 2004 did researchers acquire the first photo evidence of a giant squid in the wild.

20. **D.** Along with laying eggs, the platypus has a spur on its hind foot that can deliver venom capable of causing severe pain in humans.

21. *What is a capon?*

A. A castrated rooster

B. A pygmy giraffe

C. A wild dog

D. An unfertilized eagle egg

22. What part of a horse is known as the "frog"?

A. Chest

B. Head

C. Hoof

D. Tail

21. **A.** Ouch. Why would a rooster be castrated? To improve the tenderness and quality of its meat. Capon is known as a luxury food.

22. **C.** The frog is the triangular mark on the bottom of a horse's hoof.

1. What was rock music's first "supergroup"—a musical act in which all of the members had already had successful careers as part of a band or solo act?

A. Cream

B. Crosby, Stills & Nash

C. Emerson, Lake & Palmer

D. Traveling Wilburys

2. What was the main course of the first TV dinner?

A. Salisbury steak

B. Turkey

C. Fried chicken

D. Macaroni and cheese

1.

A. Eric Clapton, Jack Bruce, and Ginger Baker were stars in their own right before they formed Cream, which released its first album in 1967. Unfortunately, the relationship soured in only two years.

2.

B. Swanson had 260 tons of leftover frozen turkey after Thanksgiving 1953, and found a clever way to turn disaster into profit: load portions of turkey, peas, sweet potatoes, and cornbread dressing onto an aluminum tray, and voila! A portable feast was born.

3. *What was the first American daily comic strip?*

A. The Katzenjammer Kids

B. Happy Hooligan

C. A. Piker Clerk

D. The Yellow Kid

4.

The first pizzeria in the world opened in Naples, Italy, in 1738. **WHAT WAS IT CALLED**

A. Atza Pizzeria

B. Angelo's Pizzeria

C. Antica Pizzeria

D. Aberto Pizzeria

3. **C.** The strip by Clare Briggs first appeared in the *Chicago American* in 1904.

4. **C.** The pizzeria features ovens lined with volcanic rock from Mount Vesuvius, and it's still in business today if you are in the neighborhood and want an "authentic" slice.

5. Who was the *first woman* to serve on the U.S. Supreme Court?

A. Ruth Bader Ginsburg

B. Sonia Sotomayor

C. Elena Kagan

D. Sandra Day O'Connor

6. Dolly, the first successfully cloned mammal, was what kind of animal?

A. Cow

B. Pig

C. Sheep

D. Chicken

5. **D.** Justice O'Connor was nominated by president Reagan in 1981 and served until 2006.

6.

C. Dolly the sheep lived only six years, 1996–2003. Her taxidermied remains, however, live on at the National Museum of Scotland.

7. The first AOL Instant Message was sent January 6, 1993, from Ted Leonsis to his wife. The IM said: *"Don't be scared...it is me. Love you and miss you."* What was her reply?

A. "LOL!"
B. No reply (she didn't understand how IM worked)
C. "Love you too."
D. "Wow...this is so cool!"

8. ## Which actress was the first Playboy centerfold?

A. Marilyn Monroe
B. Jayne Mansfield
C. Bettie Page
D. Barbara Windsor

7. **D.** No word on whether either punctuated their messages with emoticons.

8. **A.** *Monroe didn't pose specifically for the men's magazine; publisher Hugh Hefner purchased a nude photo of the actress from another source for his inaugural 1953 issue.*

9. Who was the first woman in space?

A. Sally Ride

B. Svetlana Savitskaya

C. Eileen Collins

D. Valentina Tereshkova

10. The first parachutist was a brave soul who plunged 3,200 feet down to what city?

A. Paris

B. London

C. Rome

D. St. Petersburg

9. **D.** Tereshkova took a space ride June 16, 1963—a full 20 years before Ride became the first American woman to duplicate the feat.

10. **A.** André-Jacques Garnerin jumped from a hydrogen balloon floating above the City of Lights on October 22, 1797.

11. *ELIZABETH TAYLOR WAS FAMOUSLY MARRIED EIGHT TIMES. WHICH OF THESE HUSBANDS WAS HER FIRST?*

A. Richard Burton

B. Conrad Hilton

C. Michael Todd

D. Larry Fortensky

12. What car make did Ray Harroun drive to victory in 1911 in **the first Indianapolis 500?**

A. Mercedes

B. Marmon

C. Mercer

D. McFarlan

11. B. The hotel heir (and great-uncle to Paris and Nicky!) was married to the actress for less than a year when she was 18.

12. B. Harroun took home a whopping $14,250 prize for winning the inaugural race.

13.

The first nuclear explosion took place in 1945 in New Mexico. What was the name of the test project?

A. Unity

B. Trinity

C. Divinity

D. Complicity

14.

Park-O-Meter No. 1, the world's first parking meter, was installed in 1935 at the corner of First Street and Robinson Avenue in what city?

A. New York City

B. Kansas City

C. Oklahoma City

D. Atlantic City

13. **B.** Trinity took place, appropriately enough, in the Jornada del Muerto (Journey of Death) desert.

14. **B.** Less than a month later, the first parking ticket was given—to a guy who swore he was just running into a store to get change for the meter. (He was a reverend, so we're inclined to believe him.)

15. Kokomo, Indiana, is known as the "City of Firsts." Which of these products was not a first for Kokomo?

A. Mechanical corn picker

B. Stainless steel

C. Computer

D. Push-button car radio

16. WHICH CITY WAS THE FIRST TO OPEN A BRANCH OF THE *U.S. STOCK EXCHANGE* ?

A. New York

B. Philadelphia

C. Washington, D.C.

D. Boston

15. **C.** *The world's first computer was developed at the University of Pennsylvania.*

16. **A.** IT OPENED IN 1790, IRONICALLY ENOUGH, AT THE LONDON COFFEE HOUSE.

17. *What was the first toy to be featured in a television commercial?*

A. Easy-Bake Oven

B. Barbie

C. Mr. Potato Head

D. Hula Hoop

18. *The first words spoken on the telephone were "Mr. Watson, come here; I want you." What were the contents of the first* telegram?

17. **C.** And the advertising paid off—the spud made more than $4 million in sales for Hasbro in just its first few months.

18.

"What hath God wrought!" read the telegram from Samuel Morse on May 24, 1844.

19. True OR false?

The Barbie doll first appeared in an astronaut uniform to commemorate Sally Ride's 1983 space shuttle mission, the first undertaken by an American woman.

20. What was the nickname given to the first TV remote control?

A. Lazy Bones

B. Spud

C. Barcalounger

D. Idle Hands

19. **FALSE.** Barbie got her astronaut on in 1965, nearly 20 years before Ride. Was it prescience—or optimism?

20. **A.** Couch potatoes everywhere rejoiced when the remote finally went public in 1956.

1. What last name would you shout if you were trying to get the attention of the first trio of brothers ever to win World Series titles?

2. Which manager was the first to win World Series titles in both leagues?

1. **Molina!** Bengie, the oldest, and Jose won championships as Los Angeles Angels teammates in 2002, and younger brother Yadier joined the club with the St. Louis Cardinals in 2006 and '11—all as catchers. Jose added another to the family trophy case as a New York Yankee in '09.

2. *Sparky Anderson captured his first two World Series championships at the Cincinnati Reds (NL) helm in 1975 and '76, and then took the Detroit Tigers (AL) to the top in '84. He was also the first manager to enjoy 100-win seasons in both leagues.*

3. WHO HOLDS THE RECORD FOR MOST CAREER HOME RUNS IN **WORLD SERIES PLAY**

A. Babe Ruth
B. Mickey Mantle
C. Duke Snider
D. Yogi Berra

4. Before the San Francisco Giants swept the Detroit Tigers in four games to win the 2012 World Series, when was the last time a National League team recorded a World Series sweep?

3. **B.** Mantle, with 18 World Series home runs, topped Babe Ruth's previous record by three.

4. **1990.** That's when the Cincinnati Reds took four straight over the Oakland Athletics.

5. *Who was the first player in Major League history to hit 30 home runs, steal 45 bases, and score 125 runs in a single season?*

A. Albert Pujols

B. Jackie Robinson

C. Barry Bonds

D. Mike Trout

6. Miguel Cabrera of the Detroit Tigers won the American League Triple Crown in 2012, leading the league in batting, home runs, and RBI. Before "Miggy," who was the last Triple Crown winner?

A. Jim Rice

B. George Brett

C. Carl Yastrzemski

D. Mickey Mantle

5. **D.** Trout made history during 2012, and he did most of the damage before celebrating his 21st birthday. His unprecedented season earned the Los Angeles Angels star the 2012 AL Rookie of the Year Award.

6. **C.** "Yaz" treated Boston Red Sox fans to a Triple Crown in 1967. It would be the last one in the Majors for 45 years before Cabrera came along.

7. *WHICH HALL OF FAMER APPEARS ON THE MOST VALUABLE BASEBALL CARD IN THE WORLD?*

A. Babe Ruth

B. Honus Wagner

C. Ted Williams

D. Ty Cobb

8. **True OR false?**

Brothers B.J. and Justin Upton hit their 100th career Major League home runs on the exact same day in 2012.

7. **B.** The 1909 Honus Wagner T-206 card, because of its scarcity, has for many years been the most valuable card on the market. One sold in 2013 for more than $2 million.

8. **TRUE.** B.J. reached the century mark on August 3, and 44 minutes later younger brother Justin hit his 100th, too. Of the five previous brother tandems to compile 100 career home runs, none ever hit homers on the same day.

9. *A whopping seven no-hitters were thrown during the 2012 season. When was the last time there were that many no-no's in a year?*

A 1991
B. 1981
C. 1971
D. 1961

10. **WHO WAS THE FIRST PITCHER IN MAJOR LEAGUE HISTORY TO LOSE A NO-HITTER?**

A. Sandy Koufax
B. Ken Johnson
C. Whitey Ford
D. Nolan Ryan

9.

A. There were also seven in 1991, including Nolan Ryan's record seventh (and final) one.

10.

B. Johnson, pitching for the Houston Colt .45s, threw a no-hitter against the Cincinnati Reds on April 24, 1964, but suffered a 1–0 defeat. Johnson threw wildly to first base on Pete Rose's bunt in the ninth inning, and a subsequent error by second baseman Nellie Fox allowed the winning run to cross.

11. Which master of the cut fastball set the Major League record for career saves in 2011?

12. Which of the following was not a public-relations stunt designed by the wacky Bill Veeck?

A. Sending 3'7" Eddie Gaedel to the plate

B. Allowing fans to make managerial decisions via cue cards

C. Putting a golf driver in a struggling player's hands

D. Disco Demolition Night in Chicago

11. Mariano Rivera, routinely throwing nothing but "cutters," broke Trevor Hoffman's mark when he notched his 602nd career save.

12. **C.** Veeck made a career out of wacky promotions, but a golf club was not among his many stunts.

13. Which former National League team moved to the American League in 2013?

14. The Los Angeles Dodgers and Boston Red Sox played a 2008 exhibition at the Los Angeles Coliseum that drew a record crowd for a pro baseball game. How many people attended?

A. 95,300

B. 105,300

C. 115,300

D. 125,300

13. The Houston Astros. After 51 years in the NL, the Astros made the unprecedented move to the AL to begin the 2013 season.

14. C. The 115,300 fans broke—by about a thousand—the previous record set at the 1956 Melbourne Olympics in Australia.

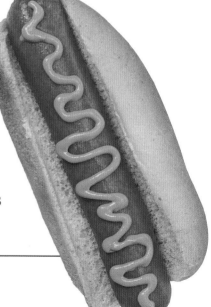

15. Which hitting machine broke George Sisler's 84-year-old Major League record for hits in a season during 2004?

16. True **OR** false?

Despite batting .406 in 1941, Ted Williams did not win the American League MVP Award that year.

15. **Ichiro Suzuki.**

The Seattle Mariners star rapped 259 hits, two more than Sisler had way back in 1920.

16. **TRUE.** *That was also the year Joe DiMaggio hit in a Major League record 56 consecutive games, and the New York Yankees star took MVP honors.*

17. *WHICH OF THESE WORLD SERIES MVPS DID NOT EARN THE HONOR AS A CATCHER?*

A. Pat Borders

B. Steve Yeager

C. Ray Knight

D. Gene Tenace

18. What nickname did Reggie Jackson earn, in part, by hitting home runs on four straight swings of the bat in the 1977 World Series?

A. Mr. October

B. The Series Slugger

C. Straw that Stirs the Drink

D. Rockin' Reggie

17. **C.** Knight played third base for the New York Mets when he won World Series MVP honors in 1986.

18. **A.** The New York Yankees slugger came to be known as Mr. October for the postseason damage he did with the bat.

19. When he wasn't butchering the English language with his unique wit, Yogi Berra could frequently be found playing in the World Series. How many times did the longtime New York Yankees catcher reach the Fall Classic?

A. 11
B. 12
C. 13
D. 14

20. *Which player, in 2000, became the first in Major League history named MVP of both the All-Star Game and World Series in the same year?*

A. Derek Jeter
B. Mariano Rivera
C. Roger Clemens
D. Alex Rodriguez

19.

D. Berra played in the World Series a record 14 times

20. **A.** Jeter accomplished the feat after going 9-for-22 with two home runs to lead the New York Yankees to a five-game World Series win over the New York Mets. He went 3-for-3 with two RBI in the All-Star Game.

21. True OR false?

"Shoeless" Joe Jackson went 12-for-32 (.375) during the 1919 World Series—the one for which he and seven Chicago White Sox teammates were banned for life for their roles in "fixing" games.

22. IN WHAT YEAR DID THE PHILADELPHIA PHILLIES WIN THEIR FIRST WORLD SERIES?

A. 1960
B. 1970
C. 1980
D. 1990

21. **TRUE.**
For someone who was allegedly trying to "throw" games, Jackson's 12 hits still stand as a record for an eight-game World Series (before the format changed to best-of-seven).

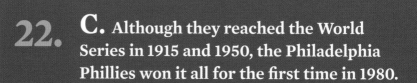

22. **C.** Although they reached the World Series in 1915 and 1950, the Philadelphia Phillies won it all for the first time in 1980.

MONEY MATTERS

1. *Can U.S. currency feature a portrait of a living person?*

2. Which of these was not an early form of currency?

A. Cows and other livestock

B. Salt and pepper

C. Water

D. Cowry shells

1. **NO.** An 1866 law prohibits the practice—hence the nickname "dead presidents" for money.

2. **C.** Animals have long been used in trade, Roman workers were paid with salt (hence the expression "worth one's salt"), and in England in the Middle Ages, rent could be paid in peppercorns.

3. What is the average life expectancy for a one-dollar bill?

A. 6 months
B. 13 months
C. 21 months
D. 29 months

4. WHICH BILL WEIGHS THE MOST: $1, $5, $10, $20, $50, or $100 **?**

3. **C.** Each year, 95 percent of new bills are printed to replace worn-out money.

4. Each bill weighs the same: **one gram.**

5. What is the largest U.S. note ever printed by the Bureau of Engraving and Printing?

A. $500 bill
B. $1,000 bill
C. $10,000 bill
D. $100,000 bill

6. *HOW MANY STATES ACCEPT PENNIES AT THEIR TOLLBOOTHS?*

5. **D.** These notes were printed in 1934 and 1935 and featured a portrait of Woodrow Wilson.

6. One. *The other 49 may not have much use for the penny, but Lincoln's home state of Illinois has a soft spot for it.*

7. Since 1787, more than 300 billion pennies have been produced. About how many are currently in circulation?

    A. 50 billion
    B. 100 billion
    C. 150 billion
    D. 200 billion

8. *The presidential profiles on the penny, the original Jefferson nickel, the dime, and the quarter all face left except for which one?*

    A. Lincoln (penny)
    B. Jefferson (nickel)
    C. Franklin Roosevelt (dime)
    D. Washington (quarter)

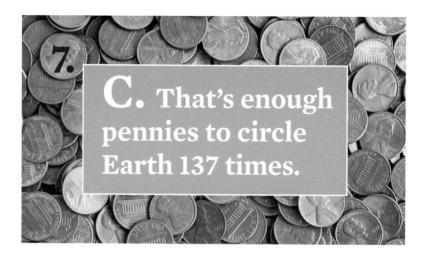

7. **C.** That's enough pennies to circle Earth 137 times.

8. **A.** People have long imagined any number of explanations for this about-face, but the disappointingly simple answer is that the sculptor was working from a photo in which Lincoln faced to the right.

9. Match the country with its currency.

1. Brazil   A. Bolívar
2. Denmark   B. Real
3. Japan   C. Krone
4. Venezuela   D. Won
5. South Korea   E. Yen

10. *Whose portrait was on the first one-dollar bill minted by the U.S. Treasury*

9.

1. **B**
2. **C**
3. **E**
4. **A**
5. **D**

10. *The honor went to Treasury Secretary Salmon P. Chase when the first bill was issued in 1862. The more recognizable George Washington dollar began to be printed in 1869.*

11. *WHAT TIME IS SHOWN ON THE INDEPENDENCE HALL CLOCK ON THE BACK OF THE $100 BILL?*

12. What do the franc, Deutsche mark, drachma, lira, guilder, escudo, and peseta have in common?

11. *Trick question!*

The clock shows 10:30 on $100 bills released in 2013 or later. Older bills still in circulation show 4:10.

12.

All were replaced as national currency by the Euro.

13. Which of these countries does not use the U.S. dollar as its currency?

A. Zimbabwe

B. Panama

C. El Salvador

D. Zambia

14. *The Chinese yuan and the Japanese yen share the same root word.* ***What does it mean?***

A. Paper

B. Round

C. Metal

D. Golden

13.

D.
**Zambia uses
the kwacha.**

14. **B.** THE WORD
WAS USED TO
DESCRIBE THE
SHAPE OF THE
COINAGE.

15. Which of the following is an example of **bullion?**

A. Silver bar

B. Beef futures

C. Bonds

D. Exchange traded fund

16. Which bill is referred to as a "C-note"?

15.

A. Although it shares the same root word with tasty broths (bouillon, meaning "boiling"), bullion refers to precious metals in bar or ingot form.

16. The $100 bill—C is the Roman numeral for 100. The bill is also sometimes called a "Benjamin," in reference to the image of Benjamin Franklin on the front.

1. **What was the end result of the Manhattan Project?**

A. An atomic bomb

B. The Brooklyn Bridge

C. A hovercraft

D. The flux capacitor

2. **The War of 1812 occurred between which two nations?**

A. France and Spain

B. Russia and the British Empire

C. The British Empire and the United States

D. France and Russia

211

1.

A. The project lasted from 1942 to early 1947 and took place simultaneously in more than 30 cities in the United States, Canada, and the United Kingdom. Manhattan was the first headquarters of the top-secret project—right across from city hall.

2.

C. All the above pairings were at war with each other in 1812, due to a little emperor named Napoleon. Ultimately, the 32-month Revolutionary War rematch resolved the remaining concerns over the United States' declaration of independence, and the U.S. and the U.K. have been close allies ever since.

3. Of the celebrated Greek philosophers—Aristotle, Plato, and Socrates—

who taught whom?

4. Which town was the scene of the Gunfight at the O.K. Corral?

A. Cimarron, New Mexico
B. Cripple Creek, Colorado
C. Dodge City, Kansas
D. Tombstone, Arizona

3. *Socrates taught Plato, and Plato taught Aristotle. You can remember the order by the acronym "SPA." Just don't confuse SPA with SAP or ASP.*

4. **D.** Actually, the famous gunfight between Wyatt Earp's crew and a group of outlaw brothers took place near the O.K. Corral, in an empty lot next to Camillus Fly's photography studio. Perhaps "Gunfight at the C.F. Studio" wasn't catchy enough.

5. ## WHAT AGE FOLLOWED THE
BRONZE AGE?

A. Ice Age

B. Iron Age

C. Stone Age

D. Age of Innocence

6. During their expedition across the American West from 1804 to 1806, explorers Meriwether Lewis and William Clark traveled with a French fur trader and his young Shoshone wife. What was her name?

A. Kateri Tekakwitha

B. Pocahontas

C. Sacagawea

D. Weetamoo

5. **B.** Characterized by the types of material being used to make tools at the time, the Stone Age is first in the Three-Age System of archaeology, followed by the Bronze Age and then the Iron Age. In Hollywood, though, Ice Age was followed by *Ice Age: The Meltdown*, *Ice Age: Dawn of the Dinosaurs*, and *Ice Age: Continental Drift*.

6. **C.** Although she did not serve as a guide for the expedition, as is often reported, Sacagawea helped foster diplomacy with Native Americans, provided input on the best routes to take, and served as an interpreter.

7. *How many wives did King Henry VIII have*

A. 5
B. 6
C. 7
D. 8

8. **HALLEY'S COMET LAST APPEARED IN 1986. WHEN IS IT SCHEDULED TO APPEAR NEXT?**

A. 2041
B. 2048
C. 2061
D. 2087

7. **B.** Henry was married six times. Probably the most famous of his wives was the ill-fated Anne Boleyn, executed in 1536. If you have trouble keeping track of all of Henry's wives, try to remember this little mnemonic device: "Annulled, beheaded, died; annulled, beheaded, survived."

8. **C.** The comet is visible from Earth every 75 to 76 years as it orbits the Sun. American author Mark Twain was born two weeks after the comet's perihelion (when it's closest to the sun) in 1835, and he predicted he would live until the comet's return. He died April 21, 1910—the day after the comet's next perihelion.

9. According to the Supreme Court decision in the case of *Brown v. Board of Education,* the *Plessy v. Ferguson* decision violated which amendment by upholding racial segregation in public schools?

A. First Amendment

B. Eleventh Amendment

C. Twelfth Amendment

D. Fourteenth Amendment

10. What was the name of the theater where President Lincoln was

ASSASSINATED?

A. Booth Theater

B. Ford's Theater

C. Lions Theater

D. Marquee Theater

9. **D.** The Equal Protection Clause of the Fourteenth Amendment states, "No state shall... deny to any person within its jurisdiction the equal protection of the laws." The Fifteenth Amendment ultimately allowed everyone to vote. (Except women—that happened 50 years later.)

10. **B.** On the night of April 14, 1865, John Wilkes Booth waited for the main character's big laugh line in Tom Taylor's play Our American Cousin: "Don't know the manners of good society, eh? Well, I guess I know enough to turn you inside out, old gal—you sockdologizing old man-trap." The audience's laughter concealed the gunshot. It's probably inappropriate to say you had to be there.

11. **Investment manager Bernie Madoff shocked Wall Street and the world when he was arrested for stealing billions of dollars from investors in a massive financial fraud. What kind of scam was this?**

12. Which war do the movies *Apocalypse Now, Full Metal Jacket, Hamburger Hill,* and *Platoon* depict?

A. Vietnam War

B. Korean War

C. Peloponnesian War

D. Crimean War

11. A Ponzi scheme. U.S. prosecutors estimated that the worldwide scheme eventually totaled $64.8 billion. Madoff pled guilty to 11 criminal charges, including wire fraud, mail fraud, and money laundering. In 2009, he was sentenced to 150 years in prison. Using that length of sentence, he'll repay his duped investors at a rate of $14 per second...if he somehow manages to live until 2159.

12. **A.** *Including* Good Morning, Vietnam *would have made it too easy.*

13. *Alcatraz Island has a rich history, beginning with its name. Alcatraz is a Spanish word that translates into what?*

A. Prison
B. Pelican
C. Paradise
D. Poet

14. **WHEN ALLIED TROOPS INVADED THE NORMANDY BEACHES ON JUNE 6, 1944, THE INVASION WENT BY WHAT CODE NAME?**

A. Operation Neptune
B. Operation Luna
C. Operation Phalanx
D. Operation Eclipse

13. **B.** Originally considered the "Evil Island" by Native Americans, the "Island of the Pelicans" has been a military garrison, a military prison, the site of a Native American civil rights occupation, and a tourist trap. Operating as a federal prison from 1934 to 1963, Alcatraz housed such notorious figures as Al Capone, Mickey Cohen, and George "Machine Gun" Kelly. Now it's home to the California slender salamander. At least those don't try to escape.

14. **A.** Likely named for the Roman god of the sea, Operation Neptune succeeded after elaborate deceptions led Adolf Hitler to believe that Allied forces planned to attack from the Straits of Dover. That operation was called Operation Bodyguard. No guessing where that name came from!

15. **What did Al Capone go to jail for?**

A. Extortion
B. Mail fraud
C. Tax evasion
D. Murder

16. *Who famously said, "That's one small step for [a] man, one giant leap for mankind"?*

A. Buzz Aldrin
B. Neil Armstrong
C. John Glenn
D. Buzz Lightyear

15. **C.** *Despite all his alleged wrongdoings, he was only ever convicted of income tax evasion in 1931 and sentenced to 11 years in prison. Capone was paroled in 1939 and succumbed to a heart attack in 1947.*

16. **B.** Armstrong was the first man to walk on the moon. Later that year, *Apollo 12* astronaut Pete Conrad, shortest member of his astronaut corps, landed on the Moon, jumped down from his lunar module, and said, "Whoopie! That may have been a small one for Neil, but it's a long one for me."

17. HOW LONG WAS THE SHORTEST WAR IN HISTORY?

A. 16 months
B. 24 weeks
C. 32 days
D. 40 minutes

18. Who was the only president to get married in the White House?

A. Martin Van Buren
B. Grover Cleveland
C. James A. Garfield
D. Warren G. Harding

17. **D.** After the pro-British sultan of Zanzibar died in 1896, a not-so-pro-British sultan took his place. The United Kingdom issued an ultimatum that resulted in a 40-minute war. Zanzibar took 500 casualties while Britain took just one. Another pro-British sultan assumed leadership of the puppet government, and Britain controlled Zanzibar for the next 67 years.

18. **B.** *Another noteworthy "one and only" fact about the man on the $1,000 bill: He's the only president to serve two non-consecutive terms. Cleveland was the 22nd and 24th president of the United States of America.*

19. What famous world event happened on *November 9, 1989?*

A. The TV show *Seinfeld* premiered.

B. The Berlin Wall fell.

C. Ayatollah Khomeini died.

D. The Tiananmen Square massacre occurred.

20. *THE ROSETTA STONE IS AN IMPORTANT ARTIFACT BECAUSE IT ALLOWED HISTORIANS TO DO WHAT?*

A. Map out pyramid interiors

B. Flatten wet papyrus

C. Translate ancient text

D. Find Mt. Olympus

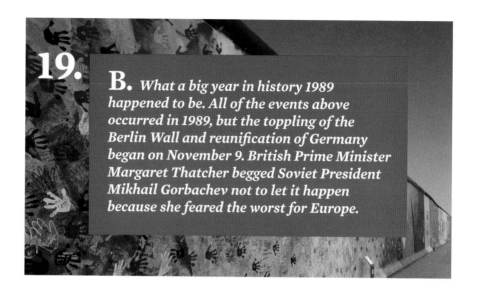

19. **B.** *What a big year in history 1989 happened to be. All of the events above occurred in 1989, but the toppling of the Berlin Wall and reunification of Germany began on November 9. British Prime Minister Margaret Thatcher begged Soviet President Mikhail Gorbachev not to let it happen because she feared the worst for Europe.*

20. **C.** The carved stone contained text written in three different ancient languages. Using their knowledge of the Greek text, linguists were able to translate the stone's older Egyptian writings and hieroglyphs. Think of it as a 1,700-pound decoder ring: the original translator app.

1. Which NBA team was the first to win at least 70 games in a season?

A. 1964–65 Boston Celtics

B. 1969–70 New York Knicks

C. 1986–87 Los Angeles Lakers

D. 1995–96 Chicago Bulls

2. Who, over 19 seasons with the Utah Jazz, became the NBA's career leader in assists?

A. Karl Malone

B. Moses Malone

C. John Stockton

D. Jason Kidd

1. **D.** Michael Jordan, Scottie Pippen, and the 1995–96 Chicago Bulls compiled a remarkable 72–10 record, becoming the first NBA team to win 70 in a season. They started the year 41–3.

2. **C.** In addition to becoming the all-time NBA assists leader, Stockton also set the career record for assists.

3. **Name the NBA's career *scoring leader.***

A. Michael Jordan
B. Kareem Abdul-Jabbar
C. Wilt Chamberlain
D. Karl Malone

4. *Which coach, in 2013, became the first ever to lead two different schools to men's NCAA Division I championships?*

A. Steve Alford
B. John Beilein
C. Jim Boeheim
D. Rick Pitino

3. **B.** With 38,387 career points, Kareem retired in 1989 with the NBA career scoring record.

4. **D.** *On the same day he learned he would be inducted into the Basketball Hall of Fame, Pitino coached Louisville past Michigan for the national title. He had taken Kentucky all the way 17 years earlier, making him the first coach ever to win titles at two different Division I schools.*

5. *WHO WAS KNOWN AS THE "WIZARD OF WESTWOOD"?*

A. John Wooden
B. Woody Hayes
C. Sean Woods
D. Bobby Knight

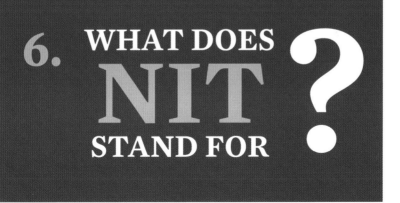
6. **WHAT DOES NIT STAND FOR ?**

5. **A.** The legendary John Wooden came to be known by this nickname while coaching UCLA to college basketball greatness.

6.

National Invitation Tournament. Originating in 1938, it predates the NCAA tournament.

7. Which came first in men's college basketball—the shot clock or the 3-point line?

8. How many national championships did UCLA win in the John Wooden coaching era?

A. Seven

B. Eight

C. Nine

D. Ten

7.

The shot clock was first, by one year. A 45-second shot clock was added in 1985–86 in an effort to increase scoring. The 3-point arc debuted in 1986–87.

8. **D.** The Bruins won ten national titles under Wooden between 1963 and '75.

9. Which of the following members of the 1982–83 NBA champion Philadelphia 76ers did not play in the American Basketball Association, which disbanded in 1976?

A. Maurice Cheeks
B. Moses Malone
C. Bobby Jones
D. Julius Erving

10. Which NBA team gave women's basketball great Ann Meyers a highly-publicized tryout in 1979?

A. Boston Celtics
B. Phoenix Suns
C. Indiana Pacers
D. Detroit Pistons

9. **A.** Cheeks played pro ball only in the NBA. The other three—comprising one heck of a frontcourt—were all former ABA standouts.

10. **C.** Meyers tried out for the Indiana Pacers but did not make the team. She went on to a successful career in broadcasting.

11. True OR false?

It was North Carolina that ended UCLA's record 88-game winning streak in 1974.

12. Who starred at center for the Los Angeles Lakers when they beat the Philadelphia 76ers in Game 6 to win the 1980 NBA Finals?

A. James Worthy

B. Moses Malone

C. Kareem-Abdul Jabbar

D. Magic Johnson

11. **FALSE.** It was Notre Dame. In fact, the Bruins' last loss before starting their amazing streak in '71 was also to the Fighting Irish.

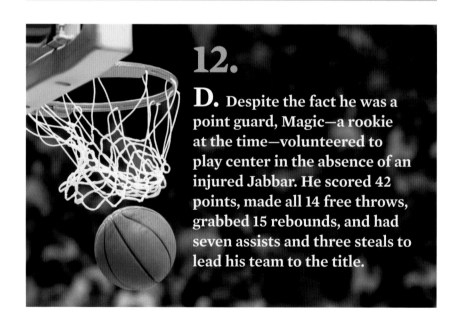

12.

D. Despite the fact he was a point guard, Magic—a rookie at the time—volunteered to play center in the absence of an injured Jabbar. He scored 42 points, made all 14 free throws, grabbed 15 rebounds, and had seven assists and three steals to lead his team to the title.

13. WHICH OF THESE GREATS IS NOT IN THE BASKETBALL HALL OF FAME FOR HIS ROLE WITH THE

BOSTON CELTICS?

A. Bill Walton

B. Jerry West

C. Bob Cousy

D. Kevin McHale

14. Which basketball power was the first to capture back-to-back titles since UCLA won seven national championships in a row in the 1960s and '70s?

A. Duke

B. North Carolina

C. N.C. State

D. UNLV

13. **B.** While the others are Boston Celtics Hall of Famers, West starred for the rival Los Angeles Lakers.

14.

A. Duke won consecutive crowns in 1991 and '92.

15. True **OR** false?

The man Duke coach Mike Krzyzewski passed to become the winningest coach in major men's college basketball history in 2011 was his friend, mentor and former coach, Bob Knight.

16. Why is a team based in Los Angeles nicknamed the **Lakers?**

15. **TRUE.** *"Coach K" played for Knight at West Point (Army) and later served as a graduate assistant under Knight at Indiana University.*

16. Because they used to play in Minnesota, the "Land of 10,000 Lakes," before becoming the NBA's first West Coast team before the 1960–61 season. The Minneapolis Lakers featured one of the league's first superstars in George Mikan.

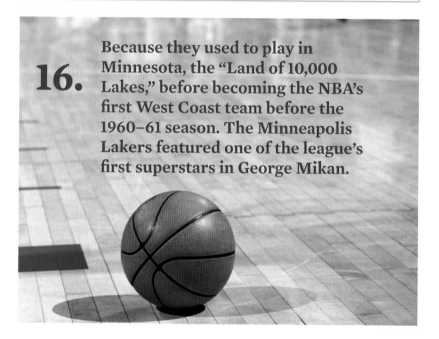

17. *Which versatile Milwaukee Bucks legend won the first two NBA Defensive Player of the Year Awards in 1983 and '84?*

A. Sidney Moncrief

B. Kareem Abdul-Jabbar

C. Marques Johnson

D. Bob Lanier

18. True OR false?

Julius Erving is the all-time scoring leader in Philadelphia 76ers history.

17. **A.** Moncrief made steals, blocked shots, and forced his matchup to work tirelessly for every look at the basket over 11 NBA seasons—10 with the Milwaukee Bucks.

18. FALSE. With 18,364 points, Erving is up there. But Hal Greer holds the franchise scoring record with more than 21,000 career points.

19.

BY WHAT NICKNAME WAS THE PHILADELPHIA 76ERS GREAT JULIUS ERVING COMMONLY KNOWN?

A. Iceman
B. Dr. Dunkenstein
C. Dr. J
D. Ace

20.

Which school, in 2004, became the first to claim both the men's and women's NCAA Division I basketball championships in the same year?

19. **C.** Dr. J operated at a level unfamiliar to his contemporaries in the 1970s and '80s, bringing an excitement and showmanship to the floor that paved the way for players like Magic Johnson and Michael Jordan.

20.

Connecticut.
The Huskies defeated Georgia Tech in the men's final, and the next day the UConn women knocked off Tennessee to double the fun.

21. *President Bill Clinton was in the crowd for the 1994 NCAA men's basketball title game, cheering on which team to a victory over Duke?*

A. Kansas

B. North Carolina

C. Arkansas

D. UNLV

22. When Connecticut coach Geno Auriemma won his eighth NCAA women's basketball championship in 2013, which legendary coach did he tie for most women's titles?

A. Vivian Stringer

B. Pat Summitt

C. Tara VanDerveer

D. Kay Yow

21. **C.** Clinton, an Arkansas native and former governor of the state, was also on hand for the Razorbacks' regional final victory against Michigan that year, becoming the first sitting president to attend an NCAA tournament game.

22. **B.** Summitt won eight national titles during her tenure at Tennessee from 1974 to 2012.

23. Which of the following players was not a member of Michigan's famed "Fab Five" class of the early 1990s?

A. Jalen Rose

B. Jimmy King

C. Rumeal Robinson

D. Chris Webber

24. True OR false?

An official NCAA women's basketball is smaller than a men's ball.

23. **C.** Robinson was the hero of Michigan's 1989 NCAA championship, hitting two free throws in OT to beat Seton Hall, but that was before the arrival of the *"Fab Five."*

24.

TRUE. The men's ball has a 30-inch maximum circumference; the women's ball has a 29-inch maximum circumference.

25. Michael Jordan led the Chicago Bulls to six NBA championships in the 1990s. How many NBA Finals MVP awards did he win along the way?

A. Six
B. Five
C. Four
D. Three

26. Wilt Chamberlain was a 51-percent career shooter from the free throw line. How many of his 32 free throw attempts did he convert during his NBA record 100-point game in 1962?

A. 12
B. 17
C. 24
D. 28

25. **A.** Yes, MJ was MVP of all six of his NBA Finals appearances after leading his team to victory in each.

26.

D. *Talk about coming up big when it counted. Wilt traded his usual bricks for swishes, hitting free throws at an .875 rate during his signature game to lead the Philadelphia Warriors past the New York Knicks, 169–147.*

1. The United States has shoreline on how many oceans?

2. Which landmark shrinks about six inches every winter?

A. Big Ben

B. Leaning Tower of Pisa

C. Eiffel Tower

D. Giralda Tower

1. **THREE.** Atlantic, Pacific, and Arctic

2. **C.** Like a swimmer in cold water, the metal tower is susceptible to temperature-induced shrinkage.

3. On September 3, 1967, Sweden switched sides— which side of the road do drivers drive on now?

4. What is the most populous city in
North America?

A. Toronto
B. New York City
C. Mexico City
D. Los Angeles

3.

The right. Just before 5:00 a.m. there was a brief country-wide traffic jam as all traffic stopped and switched sides before heading off to start the workday.

4. **C.** With a population of 8.85 million, Mexico City beats out all the competition.

5. **In which ocean can you find a massive "island" made entirely of garbage?**

A. Indian
B. Pacific
C. Atlantic
D. Arctic

6. True OR false?

The Dead Sea is the world's saltiest body of water.

5.

B. The Great Pacific Garbage Patch covers an area about 100 feet deep and as much as one and a half times the land area of the United States. That is a hefty amount of garbage.

6.

FALSE. *The Dead Sea's salinity is 340 grams per liter, but Lake Asal in the East African country of Djibouti blows that out of the water with a salinity of 400 grams per liter. But before you think about bobbing in its curative waters, keep in mind that Lake Asal has a salt crust up to 13 inches thick along its "shore"—thick enough to drive a car on!*

7. *Which is the only city in the world to have turned down a chance to host the Olympics?*

A. Denver, Colorado, USA
B. St. Petersburg, Russia
C. Istanbul, Turkey
D. Madrid, Spain

8. *THE DEEPEST AREA IN THE WORLD'S OCEANS SHARES A NAME WITH WHICH SPACE SHUTTLE?*

A. Atlantis
B. Challenger
C. Columbia
D. Discovery

7.

A. Residents of the Mile-High City took to the ballot and voted against holding the 1976 Winter Games in their city. Not to worry, though— the city and state have formed a committee to consider a bid for the 2022 Winter Games.

8.

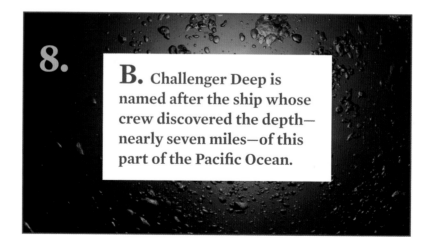

B. Challenger Deep is named after the ship whose crew discovered the depth— nearly seven miles—of this part of the Pacific Ocean.

9. WHAT EUROPEAN CAPITAL IS HOME TO MORE DOGS THAN *PEOPLE?*

A. London
B. Berlin
C. Paris
D. Amsterdam

10. Where is the world's largest ice skating area?

A. Ottawa, Ontario, Canada
B. Vaasa, Finland
C. Moscow, Russia
D. Nuuk, Greenland

9. **C.** When visiting the French capital, attention à la marche *(watch your step)*.

10. **A.** If you've got the time and the stamina, you can skate 4.8 miles on Ottawa's Rideau Canal Skateway.

11. What is the most remote island in the world?

A. Saint Helena
B. Bouvet Island
C. Easter Island
D. Kiribati

12. *The G8 is a group of eight powerful countries whose representatives meet each year to try to solve global problems. How many of the eight countries can you name?*

11.

B. This South Atlantic island is almost a thousand miles away from its closest neighbor, Queen Maude Land, Antarctica. If you need to borrow a cup of sugar, though, you're out of luck—the island is uninhabited.

12.

Canada, France, Germany, Italy, Japan, Russia, United Kingdom, and United States

13. WHAT IS THE ONLY ONE OF THE SEVEN WONDERS OF THE ANCIENT WORLD STILL IN EXISTENCE?

14. What is the collective name for the vast rural areas of Australia

A. Great Plains

B. Big Steppes

C. Outback

D. Centrelands

13. The Great Pyramid of Giza. The other six wonders—the Colossus of Rhodes, the Hanging Gardens of Babylon, the lighthouse at Alexandria, the mausoleum at Halicarnassus, the statue of Zeus at Olympia, and the Temple of Artemis at Ephesus—are lost to the sands of time.

14. **C.** It's not just a steakhouse! The Outback is also nicknamed "the back of beyond" and "beyond the black stump."

15. *What is the capital of Turkey?*

A. Ankara
B. Istanbul
C. Bursa
D. Adana

16. Which is the largest continent?

A. North America
B. Antarctica
C. Africa
D. Asia

15. **A.** This planned city beat out its big sister Istanbul because of its position right in the center of the country—much to the Turkish delight of its residents!

16. **D.** Asia is the largest both by land mass (44,579,000 square miles) and population (4 billion).

17. True **OR** false?

There are two European countries that are smaller than New York's Central Park.

18. Which South American country is home to the ancient city of Machu Picchu?

A. Brazil

B. Colombia

C. Bolivia

D. Peru

17. **TRUE.** *Central Park covers 1.3 square miles, while Monaco covers 0.7 square miles and the tiny nation of Vatican City only occupies 0.2 square miles.*

18.

D. The ancient home of the Inca Empire used to be a six-day walk from civilization, but now train travelers can leave from Cusco and get there in mere hours.

19. Amsterdam is sometimes called the *"Venice of the North."* How many canals does it have?

A. 55
B. 105
C. 165
D. 215

20. WHAT IS THE ONLY COUNTRY WITH A FLAG THAT IS NOT RECTANGULAR OR SQUARE?

A. Yemen
B. Nepal
C. Switzerland
D. Mexico

19.

C. And along with the canals are 1,281 bridges, most of which open to let ships pass through and provide Dutch schoolchildren with a handy "The bridge was open" excuse for tardiness. Hey, it beats "The dog ate my homework."

20. **B.** Nepal's flag is made of two joined triangular shapes with sun and moon designs.

AMERICANA

1. **What is the official state sport of Maryland?**

A. Jousting

B. Shuffleboard

C. Dressage

D. Sailing

2. **We're used to seeing portraits of George Washington with a powdered wig. What color was his hair underneath it?**

A. Blonde

B. Brown

C. Black

D. Red

1. **A.** No word on whether Medieval Times is the official restaurant, though.

2. **D.** Washington was a carrot-top! Thomas Jefferson and Martin Van Buren round out the presidential redhead contingent.

3. **Hawaii has eight major islands.**
How many can you name?

4. **This'll perk you right up! Which of these is not a real town named after America's favorite caffeinated beverage?**

A. Hot Coffee, Mississippi

B. Coffeeville, Alabama

C. Coffee Creek, Montana

D. Coffee Cup, Washington

3.

Hawaii (the Big Island), Kahoolawe, Kauai, Lanai, Maui, Molokai, Niihau, and Oahu

4. **D.** But it's a sponsorship opportunity for Starbucks!

5. Connecticut was the first state to set a speed limit. At what "blazing" speed would cars hit that limit?`

A. 5 miles per hour

B. 7 miles per hour

C. 9 miles per hour

D. 12 miles per hour

6. *IN WHICH SOUTHERN STATE CAN YOU FIND THE TOWNS REPUBLICAN AND DEMOCRAT?*

A. North Carolina

B. Georgia

C. South Carolina

D. Arkansas

5. **D.** Outside of city limits, however, cars could travel at the breakneck pace of 15 miles per hour.

6. **A.** *Though each party is known for digging in its Tar Heels when debate season rolls around.*

7. True OR false?

At least one early president was a big fan of skinny-dipping.

8. Colonel Sanders (of KFC fame) was named an honorary Kentucky Colonel by the state's governor, and he's in good company. Which of these figures was not made an honorary Kentucky Colonel?

A. Muhammad Ali

B. Pope John Paul II

C. Al Gore

D. Whoopi Goldberg

7. **TRUE.** John Quincy Adams started each summer day with a swim au naturel in the Potomac River.

8. **C.** It's hard to imagine this group sitting on the veranda drinking mint juleps together.

9. Which state is home to the only active diamond mine in the United States?

A. Montana
B. Arkansas
C. West Virginia
D. Oklahoma

10. The United States has never lost a war in which what were used?

A. Torpedoes
B. Horses and bayonets
C. Cannons
D. Mules

9. **B.** At Crater of Diamonds State Park, it's finders keepers (after a small entry fee, naturally). *Can you dig it?*

10. D. Presumably the mules were just too stubborn to give up.

11. **In which hand does the Statue of Liberty hold a torch?**

12. *Which animal-named city is the cow-chip-throwing capital of the world?*

A. Buffalo, New York

B. Beaver, Oklahoma

C. Porcupine, South Dakota

D. Alligator, Mississippi

11. **RIGHT.** In the statue's left hand is a tablet inscribed with the date July IV MDCCLXXVI—July 4, 1776—to commemorate American independence.

12. **B.** BYOC (Bring Your Own Chips) for this can't-miss competition each April.

13. *Before it was settled in Washington, D.C., the U.S. capital was in eight other cities. Which of these did not serve as the capital?*

A. Philadelphia, Pennsylvania

B. Montpelier, Vermont

C. Trenton, New Jersey

D. Baltimore, Maryland

14. True OR false?

Hugh Hefner saved the famous Hollywood sign by hosting a fund-raiser at the Playboy Mansion.

13. **B.** Montpelier, Vermont did not serve as the U.S. capital. Lancaster, Pennsylvania; York, Pennsylvania; Princeton, New Jersey; Annapolis, Maryland; and Manhattan, New York also took turns as the nation's capital.

14. **TRUE.** *Hefner offered stars the chance to "adopt" the letters of the sign for $27,500 each, and started things off by adopting the Y himself. Actor Gene Autry bought an L. Rocker Alice Cooper saved an O. The rebuilt sign was unveiled in November 1978.*

15. Which woman is the subject of the most American **statues?**

A. Sacagawea

B. Sojourner Truth

C. Annie Oakley

D. Amelia Earhart

16. *WHICH OF THESE "ALPHABET AGENCIES" WAS NOT PART OF THE NEW DEAL?*

A. CCC

B. FDIC

C. SEC

D. CDC

15. **A.** And if you need to settle a dispute, you can always flip a golden Sacagawea dollar.

16. **D.** The Centers for Disease Control and Prevention (CDC) was established in 1946, about 10 years after the Great Depression and the start of the New Deal agencies. The Civilian Conservation Corps (CCC), Federal Deposit Insurance Corporation (FDIC), and Securities Exchange Commission (SEC) were part of the New Deal.

17. *The proud American motto "E pluribus unum"—out of many, one—was originally used by the ancient Roman poet Virgil to describe what foodstuff?*

A. Lasagna

B. Salad dressing

C. Pizza

D. Dessert wine

18. **How many spikes are there in the Statue of Liberty's crown?**

17. **B.** No word on whether Virgil preferred oil and vinegar over ranch.

18. Seven, SYMBOLIZING THE SEVEN SEAS.

19. What is President Barack Obama's Secret Service code name?

A. Rogue

B. Renegade

C. Rambo

D. Rascal

20. IN WHAT MAJOR CITY CAN YOU FIND THE **MAGNIFICENT MILE** ?

A. Chicago

B. New Orleans

C. Seattle

D. New York

19. **B.** The whole Obama family has "R" code names: Michelle is Renaissance, while daughters Malia and Sasha are Radiance and Rosebud, respectively.

20. **A.** This famous shopping destination sprawls along Michigan Avenue in the *WINDY CITY.*

1. Which inventor acted as a tutor to Helen Keller, the young girl who could not see, hear, or speak?

A. Alexander Graham Bell

B. Thomas Edison

C. Antonio Meucci

D. Elisha Gray

2. In Roald Dahl's children's book of the same name, to what does The BFG refer?`

A. Belly Flop Gang

B. Best Friends Guild

C. Brain Freeze Gulp

D. Big Friendly Giant

1. **A.** Keller went on to dedicate her autobiography *The Story of My Life* to the man who invented the first practical telephone, the metal detector, and the hydrofoil.

2. **D.** Standing 24 feet tall, the BFG's main job was to deliver good dreams to children. He first appeared in Dahl's *Danny, the Champion of the World*. Too bad he didn't show up in Dahl's James Bond script *You Only Live Twice*.

3. *Which of the following characters NEVER appeared in J.R.R. Tolkien's The Lord of the Rings trilogy?*

A. Meriadoc

B. Ahsoka

C. Faramir

D. Elrond

4. What distinguishes French painter Monet from French painter Manet, aside from the vowel in their names? Match each fact to one of the painters.

A. Painted outdoor scenes and people while in a studio

B. Painted what he saw while outdoors

C. Was married twice and tried to commit suicide in between marriages

D. Married his father's mistress and died from heumatism, gangrene, and syphilis

3. **B.** Meriadoc was the Hobbit better known as Merry, Faramir was the human Boromir's brother, and Elrond was the elf lord. Ahsoka is Anakin Skywalker's apprentice in the TV show *Star Wars: The Clone Wars*...and maybe the future movies?

4. *Claude Monet was fond of painting outdoor scenes (B) and was married twice (C); Monet tried to end it all because he wasn't making money, but at the end of his life he did all right for himself. Edouard Manet primarily painted while indoors (A) and had an unpleasant demise (D); it's even possible that Manet's son might actually have been his brother.*

5. **Richard Bachman is the alter ego of which famous author?**

A. Stephen King

B. John Grisham

C. Tom Wolfe

D. John Updike

6. In Ray Bradbury's *Fahrenheit 451*, books are so illegal that, if you're found with one, firefighters will burn down your house. Which of these books didn't Ray Bradbury write?

A. *Dandelion Wine*

B. *The Martian Chronicles*

C. *The Door into Summer*

D. *Something Wicked This Way Comes*

5. **A.** King chose the name Richard after crime novelist Donald E. Westlake's pseudonym, Richard Stark, and Bachman for the band Bachman-Turner Overdrive. He started writing under the pen name to test whether it was his talent or his name that sold books. He wrote four novels (*Rage, The Long Walk, Roadwork,* and *The Running Man*) before being discovered. King continues to reference his most lifelike creation to this day.

6. **C.** The Door into Summer *was written by Bradbury contemporary Robert A. Heinlein in 1956. Bradbury's seasonally titled* Farewell Summer *was published in 2006; Bradbury passed away six years later. Farewell, Ray.*

7. *WHAT DOES THE "J" STAND FOR IN AUTHOR J. K. ROWLING'S NAME?*

A. Jane

B. Joanne

C. Joely

D. Judy

8. *Destino* is a Walt Disney-produced animated short film released in 2003. Its actual production began in 1945 and featured work by Disney himself and what famous artist?

A. Salvador Dali

B. Pablo Picasso

C. Henri Matisse

D. Max Ernst

7. **B.** *The initials stand for Joanne Kathleen, but the Harry Potter author usually goes by "Jo."*

8. **A.** While preparing for *Fantasia 2000*, Walt's nephew Roy E. Disney stumbled across the unfinished project and championed its completion. Disney added computer animation alongside the original footage. It's a meeting of the generations. A true Surrealist moment, it was...*Destino*.

9. Who sculpted the famous statue *David*, supposedly the representation of the ideal male body?

A. Botticelli
B. Michelangelo
C. Francesco da Sangallo
D. Leonardo da Vinci

10. Which author created the **LAND OF OZ** ?

A. Roald Dahl
B. J.R.R. Tolkien
C. L. Frank Baum
D. C.S. Lewis

9.

B. Take that, Mike "the Situation." You may think you have abs of steel, but *David* has equally well-sculpted abs of marble—and he's more than 500 years old.

10.

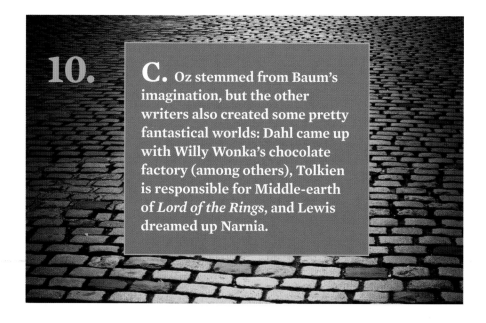

C. Oz stemmed from Baum's imagination, but the other writers also created some pretty fantastical worlds: Dahl came up with Willy Wonka's chocolate factory (among others), Tolkien is responsible for Middle-earth of *Lord of the Rings*, and Lewis dreamed up Narnia.

11. *Architect Antoni Gaudí was considered a modernista. He was inspired by the shapes of tree trunks and human bones as well as the classic Gothic style, and he incorporated all three into his designs. In which country will you find his work?*

A. France
B. Spain
C. Turkey
D. Italy

12. *OPRAH WINFREY FAMOUSLY GOT INTO A FIGHT WITH WHICH AUTHOR ON HER TALK SHOW?*

A. Dave Eggers
B. Jonathan Franzen
C. James Frey
D. Jonathan Safran Foer

11. **B.** Do one of two things immediately. Check out the amazing photographs of his buildings online—or fly to Barcelona, Spain.

12.

C. When Oprah discovered that the author of the self-purported memoir *A Million Little Pieces* had lied about parts of his life in the novel, she was outraged. She said she felt "duped" and proceeded to give him a very public verbal whoopin'.

13. Which book uses exactly 50 different words?

14. Which American pop artist is known for his paintings that resemble large comic strips?

A. Keith Haring

B. David Hockney

C. Roy Lichtenstein

D. Andy Warhol

13. **Dr. Seuss's *Green Eggs and Ham.*** *Seuss's editor bet him he couldn't write a book using 50 words or less. Guess what? The editor lost.*

14. **C.** All four are leaders of the pop art movement, but only Lichtenstein created oversize paintings in the style of bold and bright traditional comic strips.

15. How did legendary playwright Tennessee Williams (*A Streetcar Named Desire, Cat on a Hot Tin Roof*) die?

A. He choked on a bottlecap.
B. He drowned in the Mississippi River.
C. He fell from a sixth-story window.
D. He was stabbed.

16. *Which 20th-century novelist was known to many by the name "Papa"?*

A. Truman Capote
B. William Faulkner
C. Ernest Hemingway
D. Kurt Vonnegut

15. **A.** Tennessee Williams, who battled alcoholism and depression for much of his life, died in 1983 at age 71 as a result of choking on the cap from a bottle of eyedrops.

16. Ask not for whom the bell tolls; it tolls for (C), Ernest Hemingway, one of the best-known and most successful novelists of the 20th century. His works include *A Farewell to Arms, To Have and Have Not,* and, yes, *For Whom the Bell Tolls,* among others.

17. Who designed the Guggenheim Museum in *New York City?*

A. Frank Gehry
B. Louis Kahn
C. Ludwig Mies van der Rohe
D. Frank Lloyd Wright

18. On which surface would you find a traditional fresco?

A. A canvas
B. A piece of pottery
C. Skin
D. A wall

17. **D.** The renowned modern-art museum showcased both Wright's affinity for the natural world and his later take on modernist architecture. It opened in 1959, after the death of both Wright and art collector Solomon Guggenheim.

18. **D.** A fresco (which means "fresh" in Italian) is a mural painted on fresh, wet plaster with natural pigments. As the plaster and paint dry, the fresco hardens and becomes permanent. Frescoes are commonly found on church walls.

19. *Match these artists with the movement with which they are most associated:*

1. Salvador Dali
2. Henri Matisse
3. Claude Monet
4. Pablo Picasso
5. Andy Warhol

A. Cubism
B. Impressionism
C. Pop Art
D. Fauvism
E. Surrealism

20. WHICH CHARACTER IS NOT FOUND IN *ALICE IN WONDERLAND?*

A. The Mad Hatter
B. The Mock Turtle
C. Tweedledum and Tweedledee
D. The White Witch

19.
1. E
2. D
3. B
4. A
5. C

20. **D.** Alice encountered the Mad Hatter, the Mock Turtle, and Tweedledum and Tweedledee on her travels through Wonderland. To bump into the White Witch, she would have needed to take a detour to the land of Narnia.

21. According to Greek legend, what was left in Pandora's box after she opened it, releasing misery and evil into the world?

A. Faith
B. Hope
C. Innocence
D. Trust

22. What color is the Arts and Literature wedge in the game Trivial Pursuit?

21. **B.** Tricky Zeus. The king of gods gave Pandora a box (well, technically it was a jar, but why quibble?) and warned her never, ever to open it. Of course he knew her curiosity would get the better of her, and indeed it did. Fortunately she was able to slam the lid shut while hope still remained.

22. **Brown.** *(Talk about trivial trivia!)*

23. Who wrote *Pride and Prejudice*?

A. Jane Austen
B. Elizabeth Bennet
C. Charlotte Brontë
D. Emily Brontë

24. Which of the following was not a pen name of Samuel Clemens (Mark Twain)?

A. W. Epaminondas Adrastus Blab
B. Sergeant Fathom
C. Thomas Jefferson Snodgrass
D. Milcent Mollins Stanwix

23. **A.** Austen wrote the widely beloved novel. The Brontë sisters contributed *Jane Eyre* (Charlotte) and *Wuthering Heights* (Emily) to the genre. Elizabeth Bennet is a figment of Austen's imagination—the main character in *Pride and Prejudice*.

24. **D.** The 19th-century humorist looked at life with a keen wit, and he never took himself too seriously either, as can be seen in his choice of aliases.